CRYING
The Mystery of Tears

Dr. William H. Frey II
with
Muriel Langseth

WINSTON PRESS

This book is dedicated to
Merton F. Utter, Ph.D. (1917-1980),
a brilliant biochemist and teacher,
in whose laboratory I earned my Ph.D. in biochemistry
and first conceived my theory of emotional crying,
and to my mother, Brena,
who first suggested crying to me as a research subject.

Acknowledgments

We wish to thank all of those who volunteered to give their tears, blood, and personal crying experiences to us to make this research possible. Without their help, the work could not have been done and this book would not have been written.

We also wish to thank our spouses and children, who survived the writing of this book. Finally, we wish to thank Marilu LaVoie, Brenda Langseth, and Kelly Laurson for their help in completing the manuscript.

Contents

Preface

When Muriel Langseth suggested I write a book on my research on emotional crying and tears in 1981, I told her I doubted there was enough data to fill an entire book. Besides, I argued, as director of the Psychiatry Research Laboratories at St. Paul-Ramsey Medical Center (SPRMC), most of my time is spent working on my principal area of research: the biochemistry of the human brain and changes in the brain that lead to Alzheimer's disease and other forms of dementia. I simply could not take on the time-consuming project of writing a book. Langseth had learned of my tear research from a Minneapolis bookstore clerk while looking for a book on emotional crying to help determine what caused her own frequent tears. The clerk told her no books on crying were listed in Bowker's *Books in Print* but showed her a magazine article which cited our tear research. That same day she contacted me, asking where she could find more information on crying and volunteered to participate in the adult crying behavior study. Langseth closely followed the progress of our tear and crying behavior research and began compiling data on emotional crying from other sources. Being a writer and a crier, she was very interested in collaborating on a book on the subject.

About a year later, after completing more research and acknowledging the continuous world-wide interest and media coverage of our work, I agreed it was time to begin work on the first book on adult emotional crying. My primary goal was to establish present knowledge and suggest directions for future research. Other writers had contacted me about coauthoring a book, but because of Langseth's great interest and firsthand experience with emotional crying, she seemed the most likely choice. I also liked her suggestion that we designate a portion of the royalties to emotional tear and crying behavior research.

This book, based primarily on my theories and research regarding human tears and adult crying behavior, includes much information about the tear and behavior studies not covered in scientific papers and articles written by me or other writers. It contains only brief references to infant, childhood, and teenage crying, or crying in those with physical or psychiatric disorders. I also did not include the numerous psychoanalytical theories of weeping, as I had originally intended, since there are enough such theories to produce another book. As the writing progressed, I decided to concentrate on the chemical and behavioral aspects of emotional crying in apparently healthy adults. While some scholars differentiate between crying and weeping, the two terms are used synonymously throughout the book for emotional crying with tears, unless otherwise specified.

The study of psychogenic lacrimation (emotional tearing) may at first seem frivolous and insignificant to some. But since it is a direct biological response to emotional stress, I feel the study of human crying and tears will lead to a better understanding of the biochemistry of emotion.

I hope this book will help place crying in its proper perspective as a normal human response to emotional stress. In addition, I hope that it will encourage you to think about your own crying and examine your reaction when others cry.

1

Why Do We Cry?

Tears, idle tears, I know not what they mean.
Alfred Lord Tennyson
The Princess

We humans weep. Strong emotions often cause tears to surface from somewhere deep within us. We weep tears of grief when a loved one dies; we weep when a relationship ends; we often weep tears of compassion after leaving the hospital room of a seriously ill friend or relative. Even those who seldom cry for personal reasons may be brought to tears in the darkness of a theater, watching a sad movie or play. Some people deliberately seek out four-hankerchief tearjerkers so they can "have a good cry." The wetter the better.

Although weeping is usually associated with sorrow, human tears appear in response to many types of emotional stress. Tears often accompany anger and arguments. After a week in which nothing seems to go right, one more annoying event—even something as trivial as a parking ticket or burnt toast—may trigger tears of bottled-up frustration. A critical remark made when we feel overworked, unappreciated, and exhausted may generate tears of disillusionment and despair.

Other emotions also cause tears to flow. An intense moving reaction to a beautiful sunset or a sensitive piece of sculpture sometimes makes our eyes well up. Music and church services are responsible for tears which some call "tears from the soul." Extremely pleasant feelings and excitement can make us weep for joy. Photographers love to catch Olympic gold medal winners bursting into tears in their moment of triumph. We cry at weddings and graduations. We cry at the miracle of birth. We cry when someone expresses sincere appreciation and love for us. We cry when we receive an especially thoughtful gift.

In the course of a lifetime, humans instinctively weep for a multitude of reasons. It's a rare person who never sheds tears of sorrow, joy, anguish, or ecstasy. Throughout the history of humankind, tears have been intertwined with the very essence of the human heart, for the ability to shed emotional tears—psychogenic lacrimation—seems to be one of the few physiological processes which separates humans from other animals.

Two Kinds of Tears

Both animals and humans constantly produce a fluid called "basal" or "continuous" tears, which keeps the surface of the eye moist and helps prevent infection. With each blink of the eyelid a tear film bathes the surface of the eye with a bacteria-fighting fluid secreted by the main lacrimal gland and by accessory lacrimal glands located in the eyelids. And when the surface of the eye is irritated, the main lacrimal gland in humans and a similar gland in other animals produce additional tears, called "reflex" or "irritant" tears. Anyone who has chopped onions is familiar with irritant tears, which dilute and flush away the strong onion vapors. When a foreign object such as a loose eyelash or grain of sand gets in our eyes, these tears help wash away the irritating invaders. Our body also produces irritant tears when our eyes are exposed to severe cold, dust, or smoke to lessen the harmful effects on the eyes. The extra tears that wash away or reduce the effects of an irritant not only protect the surface of the cornea but also help restore normal vision as soon as possible.

Healthy eyes and clear vision are important to survival, so it's easy to understand why evolution favored the biological processes that produce both continuous and irritant tears. Alan Jordan and Jules Baum, two ophthalmologists, have recently suggested that basal or continuous tears are also produced in response to irritation of the eye and eyelids by sensory stimuli.[1] Thus basal or continuous tears may also be due to irritant tearing.

Many Questions

But what about the tears that are uniquely human, the ones generated by emotion and deep feelings? What good are tears shed when the family dog dies? or a lover leaves? or your daughter gets engaged? or your boss blames you for something beyond your control? or your friends throw a surprise birthday party for you? What value are tears shed in agony or in joy? How can tears help a lost hope? Why don't humans just express their anguish like other animals by whimpering or crying out?

Nature gradually phases out biological functions that are no longer necessary for survival. So the ability to shed emotional tears must have a specific physiological function. But what is their purpose? How and why do tears come? What triggers tears of joy and grief and frustration and anger? Why did the ability to shed tears in response to strong emotion evolve only in humans? Are emotional and reflex tears chemically different? Are tears of anguish different from tears of rapture? How often do normal people cry? Why do some people cry easily while others rarely—if ever—cry, even if they try? Why do women cry more than men? Do people feel better or worse after crying? Does our crying behavior affect our health? Does weeping indicate a weakness in our character, or is it a natural, healthful way to relieve stress? Is it wise to swallow hard and hold back our tears, or are we better off when we let go and allow the tears to spill over? What price, if any, do we pay for a stiff upper lip?

I became curious about these and many other questions concerning crying when I was a graduate student in the Department of Biochemistry at Case Western Reserve University in the early 1970s. My mother originally had brought the subject of crying to my attention as a possible area of research. Also, it occurred to me that I hadn't cried since I was about twelve years old, and I wondered whether my complete lack of crying was healthy and normal. As a bio-chemist, I was interested in learning the biological purpose of emotional tears. I went to the library to check the medical journals for information on emotional crying, thinking the answers to my questions could be found in the scientific litera-ture. After all, emotional tearing is an excretory process, I thought; so I assumed its function would have been thor-oughly investigated. The other excretory processes such as exhaling, urinating, and defecating have been studied and written about ad nauseum.

Few Answers

I found that medieval physiologists thought tears were a means of ridding the body of bad humors—fluids that cause melancholy moods. I discovered that researchers had done extensive chemical analyses of reflex and continuous tears; scientists had described the external manifestations of emo-tional crying from tearing to uncontrolled sobbing; and I found numerous views which indicated that "having a good cry" was an effective way to alleviate stress. There are a multitude of references to human weeping in history, litera-ture, and mythology. In fact poets, lyricists, and writers have covered the subject of human weeping extensively. But I found an incredible absence of scientific research on psycho-genic lacrimation and its physiological role in our lives. For some reason, human crying behavior and psychogenic tears have been virtually ignored by both biomedical and psycho-logical researchers. Perhaps they have avoided the subject of human weeping because emotions and emotional stress are hard to qualitatively define and quantitatively measure, and scientists don't like to study such poorly defined and difficult to measure phenomena. Consequently, my search for infor-mation on emotional crying produced far more questions than answers.

A few theories which attempted to explain the purpose of human weeping propose that it is simply a device to commu-nicate a need. In 1932 E. Treacher Collins stated that the purpose of weeping is "to attract attention with the object of eliciting aid and sympathy." He surmised that weeping was an outlet for nervous energy and that communication is its primary purpose.[2] In his 1942 book on the vertebrate's eye, Gordon Lynn Walls professed that psychogenic weeping "serves no physiological purpose whatever. Its value is wholly psychological and economic—as every woman knows!"[3] Wilson Mizner shared Walls' view of tears in his often quoted phrase: "The most efficient water power in the world—women's tears." And Thomas Hobbes wrote, "They are most subject to [weeping] that rely on helps external, such as women and children." (Imagine what the *Ms* editorial department would have done with those statements if they had been made in the 1980s!)

Others in the field of psychology agree with Treacher's, Walls', and Hobbes' contention that humans weep solely to communicate. Even though tears often do serve an important communication function and may help elicit "aid and sympathy," and even though some people may try to use tears to manipulate others, this explanation of crying as a psychological ploy does not adequately explain the tears. Other animals clearly communicate their needs and wants with expressive body language and by crying with whines, whimpers, yelps, and screeches without tears; and newborn humans communicate important needs to their parents using crying sounds often without tears. And if weeping is only a form of communication, why do humans shed tears in solitude? I know from my own experience that humans cry alone and that tears sometimes come as a total surprise to the weeper.

For example, one night I was sitting alone recalling pleasant moments with my grandparents, who are now quite old. An unexpected wave of sadness passed through me when I realized that my own young children would never really know my grandparents and would never experience their warmth, love, and wisdom that had added so much to my childhood. Suddenly, tears began trickling down my face. At that time I had seldom cried and was quite surprised by what was happening. I even ran to a mirror to assure myself that the wet drops running down my face were tears. My surprising tears shed in solitude that night appeared for reasons other than to communicate a want or need. No one else was in the house.

Another psychological theory of emotional crying was offered by L. Börje Löfgren in 1965. He wrote that "weeping is an act whereby aggressive energy is dissipated in secretory behaviour." He considered the release of tears as a neutralizing process that gets rid of internalized aggression occurring after a loss, which the sufferer has been unable to discharge in any other way.[4] Theories similar to Löfgren's psychoanalytical explanation of emotional tears and crying are not uncommon in the literature. Other psychological theories associate weeping with a change in one's emotional state such as when one feels relief after anquish, pain, fear, or other strong feelings.

In addition to the theories presented by psychologists and sociologists, two prominent anthropologists have proposed theories about crying and emotional tears. Charles Darwin surmised that when humans cry, the blood vessels of the eye become engorged and the surrounding muscles contract to protect it, which, he incorrectly speculated, stimulates the lacrimal glands to secrete tears. In 1872 in the book *The Expression of the Emotions in Man and Animals,* Darwin distinguished between the relief of suffering that comes from the total act of weeping, and emotional tears themselves. Darwin viewed the tears as "an incidental result, as purposeless as the secretion of tears from a blow outside the eye. . . ."[5] This concept of emotional tears by Darwin and others as an insignificant accompaniment to emotional crying was widely accepted for almost a century.

While this theory has some merit, it seems unable to adequately explain the unique evolution of emotional tears in the human being. Darwin spent his life collecting evidence that evolution does not favor purposeless processes and phases out those which are no longer necessary for the survival of a species. While I agree with Darwin's premise that the overall crying process relieves suffering, it seems very unlikely that emotional tears would survive the pressures of natural selection if they were "incidental and purposeless."

Anthropologist Ashley Montagu presented a more physiological theory of psychogenic lacrimation in 1960. He proposed that weeping originated as a protective mechanism for the normal functioning of the nasopharynx—especially in infants. In an article in the *Journal of the American Medical Association,* Montagu points out that the intake and expulsion of air that accompanies crying would quickly dry out the sensitive mucuous membranes of the nose and throat if tears did not keep them moist. When we cry, some of our tears drain through the nasolacrimal ducts, which lead from the eyelids to the nose and throat. He reasoned that tears—which contain lysozyme, an anti-bacterial enzyme—prevent dehydration of the mucous membranes and reduce the risk of contracting upper respiratory infections. The process of natural selection favors tears, Montagu concludes, because those who could produce tears were more capable of warding off infection and thus survived. Tearless babies, Montagu speculates, would have "less chance of surviving than those who cried with tears."[6]

Newborns must be excluded from the theory that emotional tears evolved to protect delicate tissues, since newborns often do not shed emotional tears until they are several days, weeks, or sometimes months old.[7] Although humans can usually shed irritant tears at birth, the ability to shed emotional tears appears to require further development. If emotional tears function solely to protect the membranes of the nose and throat from dehydration, why hasn't nature provided this protection during the first critical days and weeks of life when crying episodes are often long, intense, frequent, energetic, and supposedly drying to the upper respiratory system? While protection of the nasopharynx may be one benefit of emotional tears, it seems unlikely that emotional tears evolved solely for this purpose.

Montagu's theory has considerable appeal when applied to infants and young children, who usually inhale and exhale a lot of air during their crying episodes. However, not all emotional crying is accompanied by an increase in the breathing rate. Humans, especially adults, often cry tears without a marked increase in breathing. Thus, the excretion of emotional tears in adults usually occurs without sobbing—the convulsive catching of the breath. Even when someone sobs, the flow of tears often precedes the sobbing rather than the tears occurring as a response to sobbing. If rapid, deep breathing requires protective tearing, why wouldn't children and adults produce tears while running or performing other strenuous exercise when the breathing rate is dramatically increased? Also, many tears shed in response to emotional stress pour over the eyelids and run down the face. What good can these tears be to our mucous membranes? In fact, Montagu's theory actually addresses what we do not see (tears draining through the nasolacrimal ducts that may cause a need to blow our nose) rather than what we do see (tears running down the cheeks) when we cry.

Another somewhat trivial explanation of emotional tears must be considered. Perhaps emotional stress causes the eyes to become irritated by changing conditions on the surface of the eye. If so, emotional tears may really be the same as reflex or irritant-induced tears. This sounds feasible until you consider several facts indicating that emotional and irritant tears are triggered by entirely different mechanisms, even though they are both produced primarily by the main lacrimal gland. A topical anesthetic applied to the surface of the eye dramatically reduces irritant-induced tearing but does not affect the lacrimal gland's secretion of tears stimulated by strong emotion. Ophthalmologists often numb the surface of the eye to enable them to examine or treat the eye without stimulating irritant tears. If the person's eyes being examined were exposed to smoke or smog before the effects of the anesthetic wore off, almost no tears would be shed, even though the surface of the eye was irritated. On the other hand, if during an examination an ophthalmologist told a woman that she was losing her sight, the topical anesthetic would not stop the emotional tears—prompted by the news of approaching blindness—from flowing. Tears stimulated by dazzling bright light, which irritates the retina, and secretory drugs, which act directly on the secretory cells of the lacrimal gland, are not affected by a topical anesthetic either. Even though all these tears come primarily from the main lacrimal gland, only irritant tears are inhibited by anesthetizing the surface of the eye.[8]

Damage to certain nerve tissue also inhibits the production of irritant tears. Persons with paralysis or severance of the trigeminal (fifth cranial) nerve, do not shed tears when their eyes are irritated. Even caustic substances or foreign objects that can damage the surface of the eye do not stimulate cleansing reflex tears. However, such persons still have the ability to shed tears stimulated by strong emotion. Interruptions in the neural pathway between certain areas of the brain and the lacrimal gland abolish psychogenic weeping but do not affect irritant tearing.[9] These differences in emotional and irritant tearing rule out the possibility that emotional tears appear because the eye becomes irritated during stressful periods.

After a two-year search of the scientific literature for data on crying and emotional tears, I still had not found satisfactory answers to most of my questions. Science has explained, to a large extent, the lacrimation process that brings tears to our eyes when chopping onions, but the more complicated function responsible for tears generated by emotional stress is not clearly understood. None of the existing theories seemed to adequately explain the unique process of emotional tearing.

Tears and Homeostasis

In the resume of his book *Stress Without Distress,* Hans Selye, the world's leading stress researcher, writes that our two primary functions from the moment we are born are to adapt to our environment and at the same time to keep our system in balance. Our bodies have very sophisticated systems to sustain homeostasis—the tendency of an organism to maintain internal equilibrium by a balance of its functions, temperature, and chemical composition. External forces—physical and emotional—constantly bombard our bodies and thus upset the delicate balance necessary for health and a sense of well-being, Selye says. Usually we are not even aware of the struggle going on within us as our bodies spring into action to try to return our cells to a normal state. Failure to keep our systems in balance can cause disease and eventually death. ". . . many maladies have no specific single cause but are the result of a constellation of factors, among which mere nonspecific stress often plays a decisive role," maintains Selye.[10] While stress is only one of many contributing causes of disease (others are pathogens, genetics, diet, etc.), it is clearly an important one.

I suggest that like the excretory processes of exhaling, urinating, perspiring, and defecating, emotional tearing may play a vital role in maintaining homeostasis by removing waste and harmful substances. All excretory functions expel something from the body such as exhaled air, urine, perspiration, and feces. Since tears are a fluid that also comes out of the body, I maintain that lacrimation can also be considered an excretory process.

One of the requirements of my doctoral training program was to present original research propositions. In 1972, I formally proposed a new theory of emotional tearing based on three primary observations:
1. Stress causes a change in our body's chemistry.
2. People generally feel better after crying.
3. Emotional tearing is an excretory process.

I proposed that perhaps the reason people feel better after crying is that they may be removing in their tears chemicals that build up as a result of emotional stress. Therefore, emotional tearing may be similar to the other excretory processes, which remove waste products or toxic materials from the body. My formal study of crying began with the theory that emotional tears play a precise and central role in helping to restore the chemical balance of the body by excreting substances produced by the body in response to stress. When someone uses the expression "to cry it out," this may be literally what occurs.

The idea that the lacrimal gland has excretory ability may seem quite surprising at first. After all, the lacrimal gland lacks the filtering apparatus of the kidney. However, our studies on the chemical composition of tears have revealed that tears contain much higher concentrations of manganese than does blood serum (see Chapter 5); so evidently the lacrimal gland has the ability to concentrate and excrete substances from the blood or other body tissues.

Further evidence that the human lacrimal gland may have excretory ability comes from an unlikely source—studies conducted on a beautiful sea bird, the double-crested cormorant. In his book *From Fish to Philosopher,* Homer Smith described an experiment conducted by biologist Knut Schmitt-Nielsen, who wanted to learn about marine birds' salt and water balance. Some sea birds are able to survive without fresh water for months—even years—at sea by deriving their water from their food, primarily fresh fish.[11] To determine what happened if the birds ingested sea water, Schmitt-Nielsen conducted experiments on double-crested cormorants, large web-footed birds (related to the large-beaked pelican) that catch fish by diving under water. By means of a stomach tube Schmitt-Nielsen fed the cormorants sea water amounting to six percent of each bird's weight. He wasn't surprised when the salt content in the birds' urine rose sharply, but he and his associates hadn't expected the other excretion that took place shortly after the excess salt entered the birds' systems: The cormorants began shedding from openings on their beaks a watery liquid which they shook off by rapidly jerking their heads.

The excretions turned out to be almost pure salt solution (much saltier than human tears) and were produced by glands located in crescent-shaped depressions in the bone above the orbit of the birds' eyes. Schmitt-Nielsen found that the albatross, common cormorant, herring gull, and Humboldt penguin also have this amazing ability to remove, concentrate, and excrete very high concentrations of salt. These glands, which proved to be much more effecive at removing the toxic concentrations of salt than were the birds' kidneys, prompted Schmitt-Nielsen to observe that ". . . the kidney is not always the most important organ of excretion. . . ."[12, 13]

Smith concluded, ". . . the capacity [of the birds' kidneys] to concentrate the urine osmotically is at best slight . . . ; consequently the salt gland serves as a safety device insuring that any excess sodium chloride, ingested as sea water or in the diet, can be disposed of without excessive loss of water."[14] The salt glands with their tremendous excretory ability are critical not only to the survival of certain marine birds but also to that of waterfowl living in alkaline environments in the great plains of North America. Removal or malfunction of the gland can lead to death.[15] In birds of the same species such as the gull, those that live nearer the sea have a larger salt gland with a richer supply of blood than those that live farther inland. Evidently, with use, the glands increase in size and excretory capability, and decrease in size when they're not needed to remove toxic levels of salt.

With these glands, evolution gave these marine birds, other waterfowl, and some reptiles an additional quick reacting apparatus to restore balance to their systems. And, interestingly, these glands have blood, nerve, and glandular characteristics very much like human lacrimal glands. The salt glands and the human lacrimal glands are thus similar in their location, cell structure, nerve supply, and ability to concentrate and excrete substances (although not the same substances)—making them biological homologues.

Key to the Chemistry of Emotion?

In searching for a better understanding of emotional stress and emotional disorders, researchers have extensively studied both blood and urine; still, we know almost nothing about the chemistry of emotion and emotional stress. However, blood and urine are both complex fluids to which virtually all of the body's organ systems contribute. Unlike blood and urine, emotional tears are by definition excreted as a direct response to emotional stress. Perhaps researchers have overlooked the most logical source of information on chemical changes that occur in response to emotional stress. Concentrating on the analysis of tears in addition to blood and urine might help determine the biochemical basis of emotions. Intensive investigations of tears could help us learn what goes on in our bodies when we feel sad, angry, depressed, anxious, or ecstatic. Since certain illnesses appear to be associated with or at least aggravated by unhealthy stress, the knowledge of chemical changes that occur during stress should lead to better treatments for these stress-related disorders. I hope my theory of emotional tears will help launch a new era in the study of the biochemistry of emotions and emotional stress. Beyond this specific theory, it is my contention that emotional tears hold the key to the chemistry of emotion. Besides possibly removing excess stress-related chemicals, we may learn that emotional tears serve other important functions. As we discover what substances are in our tears, new areas of research on the biochemistry of emotion will be developed.

Dr. Balduin Schwarz, an Austrian professor who shares my interest in emotional crying, sent me the following stanza of "The Complaint" by Edward Young written in 1760.

Lorenzo! Hast thou ever weigh'd a Sigh?
Or study'd the Philosophy of Tears?
(A Science, yet unlectur'd in our Schools!)
Hast thou descended deep into the Breast,
And seen their Source? If not, descend with me,
And trace these briny Riv'lets to their Springs.

Almost two centuries later the philosophy of tears is still a science basically "unlectur'd in our schools," and investigators have done little to discover the reasons for their existence. As is the case in most research, lack of funds is the major barrier in our attempt to analyze tears and study crying behavior. However, with a limited budget, my colleagues and I have begun an extensive investigation to determine the role of human emotional crying. The result of our studies, so far, as well as research on crying conducted by other investigators, will be covered in the following chapters. We and other researchers all over the world are just beginning a long overdue quest to "trace these briny Riv'lets to their Springs."

2

The Source of Our Tears

Tears are humors from the brain.

Hippocrates

Before going into the research on tears and emotional crying behavior, I believe a summary of what is known about the physiology of the lacrimal system is necessary. I hope this concise account of how the lacrimal system works will make the results of our research more interesting and meaningful to you.

Lacrimal Secretory System

The process by which the lacrimal glands produce tears, that is, lacrimation, consists of two parts: the secretory and the excretory. The secretory system is made up of the main and accessory lacrimal glands. The main lacrimal gland, located in a depression called the lacrimal fossa in the outer upper quadrant of the bony structure surrounding the eyes, is divided into two parts: the orbital lobe and the palpebral lobe. The larger orbital lobe is fixed to the frontal bone above the outer corner of the eye. The smaller palpebral lobe, located beneath the outer upper eyelid, is fairly mobile and can be partially seen with some effort when the upper eyelid is pulled back while looking for a foreign object in the eye.

About sixty tiny glands, often referred to as accessory glands, are located in the linings of the eyelid (conjunctiva) with the majority of them lying in the outer portion of the lining of the upper lid. The function of these glands is to help secrete the stratified tear film that lubricates, protects, nourishes, and fights infection on the surface of the eye. This three-layered film is secreted by specific types of glands: mucin, lacrimal, and oil.

The inner mucin (referring to mucous) layer of the tear film which plays an important role in lubricating the eyelid, is secreted by the glands of Manz, the crypts of Henle, and the goblet cells in the conjunctiva. The main lacrimal gland and the accessory glands—the glands of Wolfing, Kraus and others—secrete the middle aqueous layer.[1] Until recently, the tear film was thought to be secreted only by the accessory glands, but research indicates that the main lacrimal gland secretes over 95% of the watery portion of the tear film.[2] Secretions that make up the outer oily later, which prevent the watery layer from evaporating quickly and running over the eyelid, come from the meibomiam glands including the glands of Zeis and Moll. The tear film in persons who lack the outer oily layer evaporates ten to twenty times faster than normal.[3] Secretion of the tear film is greatly diminished in darkness and during sleep.

Lacrimal Excretory System

Following secretion from the lacrimal glands, the tears are transported to the surface of the eye by the lacrimal excretory ducts. With each blink of the eyelid, a stream of tears is swept across the eye toward small openings (puncta) located at the nasal edge of the upper and lower eyelid. Some of the tear fluid flows along the lacrimal river (the space between the eyeball and the eyelid) toward the puncta. The tears move into a small lacrimal canal connected to a larger channel called the lacrimal sac, which gradually becomes the narrower nasolacrimal duct. This duct opens onto the mucous membranes of the nose and throat where the tears are probably reabsorbed.

Irritant and psychogenic tears secreted by the main lacrimal gland follow the same pathways as the continuous tears and also eventually end up in the nasopharyngeal mucosa. If the lacrimal gland secretes more tears than the nasolacrimal ducts can accommodate, we have "watery eyes," which are tears pooled in the lacrimal lakes—triangular spaces at the inner and outer corners of the eye. When the lacrimal lakes fill and overflow, the tears spill over the eyelid and run down the face.[4]

Too Many or Too Few

If the three-layered tear film is adequate, humans may go through life without giving any thought to its lubricating and protecting functions. However, those persons who secrete an insufficient or an overabundant amount of tear fluid are only too well aware of their continuous tears. The irritating, often painful, dry eye syndrome of hyposecretion can occur as an isolated problem or in syndromes such as Sjögren's disease, where both salivary and lacrimal secretions can be diminished.[5] Hypersecretion of tears by the lacrimal glands often occurs in allergies and other ailments causing tears to overflow. Inflammation that may cause temporary blockage of the nasolacrimal ducts also causes tears to overflow instead of draining normally; permanent blockage of these ducts results in a continuous overflow of tears—a condition called epiphora.

The Autonomic Nervous System

The principal innervation that stimulates the lacrimal glands to secrete irritant tears is understood, but much remains to be learned about the process that activates the production of tears in response to strong emotion. Before discussing how the nervous system acts on the lacrimal gland to stimulate tears, let's briefly review the basic function of the autonomic nervous system, which controls tear production.

Unlike the somatic nervous system, which produces conscious movement in skeletal muscles, the autonomic nervous system basically is controlled by the central nervous system at a subconscious level. Generally, the autonomic nervous system regulates smooth (involuntary) muscles, cardiac muscles, and glands. The network of nerve cells in the autonomic nervous system connects the brain with other areas of the body relaying vital orders that keep the body in balance and thus in good working order. This system affects respiration, digestion, circulation, metabolism, and virtually all body systems; and it can be influenced by thoughts and emotions.

The autonomic system is divided into the sympathetic and parasympathetic systems. The sympathetic system enables swift response to emergencies, as it prepares the body for "fight or flight." Fear, rage, rapture, or any strong emotion also stimulates the sympathetic system which readies the body to release energy and adapt to changes in the environment. Sympathetic impulses stimulate the adrenal medulla to produce epinephrine, which increases the heart rate and blood pressure; it dilates the skeletal muscles, bronchial tubes, and pupils of the eyes and causes raised hair, goosebumps, and increased perspiration. With its primed muscles and focused attention, the body is ready for action. At the same time, the sympathetic impulses slow down those body functions unnecessary for immediate action by inhibiting secretions of the stomach, intestines, liver, pancreas, and the salivary and lacrimal glands.

In many ways the parasympathetic works in direct opposition to the sympathetic system. For example, sympathetic impulses increase heart activity; parasympathetic impulses slow it down. Sympathetic impulses inhibit digestion; parasympathetic impulses stimulate digestive action. Sympathetic impulses inhibit lacrimal secretions under certain conditions; parasympathetic impulses stimulate lacrimal secretion. In other words, one of the primary functions of the parasympathetic system is to counteract and complement the sympathetic system by making the necessary biochemical adjustments to return body function to normal following stress.

Most sympathetic nerve cells produce norepinephrine, a neurotransmitter which relays messages between neurons. Impulses for parasympathetic stimulation are mainly transmitted between neurons by a substance called acetylcholine.

The effects of acetylcholine are much shorter and more local-ized than those of the primary sympathetic neurotransmitter, norepinephrine, which may enter the bloodstream, causing the effects of sympathetic stimulation to last longer and be more pervasive than parasympathetic stimulation.[6]

Both the sympathetic and parasympathetic nervous sys-tems appear to control the lacrimal system. While the acces-sory lacrimal glands appear to have no outside nerve supply, an abundant supply of nerve fibers innervate the main lacri-mal gland through branches of the fifth cranial (trigeminal) nerve, the seventh cranial (facial) nerve, and the cervical sympathetic chain. Excitement of the sensory receptors located on the skin near the eye, the surface of the eye, or the nasal mucousa initiates a reflex that eventually causes the lacrimal gland to produce irritant tears. So when a grain of sand blows into our eyes or when we enter a smoke-filled room, nerve cells on the surface of the eye and nasal mucosa send a message that hazardous objects or substances threaten the well-being of the eyes. This message travels from the surface nerve endings along branches of the fifth cranial nerve to the lacrimal nucleus in the brain stem. The lacrimal nucleus, thought to be the parasympathetic center for the lacrimal gland, sends a return message along branches of the seventh cranial nerve to the lacrimal gland directing it to produce tears to wash away or dilute the irritating object or substance. The nerve fibers that carry the impulses to the lacrimal gland are part of the parasympathetic nervous system.[7]

Crocodile Tears

The neural pathway that innervates the lacrimal gland is situated near the salivary nucleus, which relays messages to the salivary gland. Some humans develop a condition called "crocodile tear syndrome" in which tears flow when the per-son salivates. This "gusto-lacrimal" reflex usually develops following an injury, disease, or surgery in the vicinity of the salivary and lacrimal nuclei. As healing occurs, the nerve fibers leading to the salivary gland are misdirected as they regenerate along the same neural pathway as the fibers which send signals to the lacrimal gland. This syndrome derived its name from the legend that crocodiles weep as they eat. Fifteenth century explorer Sir John Hawkins allegedly reported, "In this river we saw many crocodiles . . . his nature is even when he would have his prey, to cry and sob. . . , to provoke them to come to him, and then he snatcheth at them."[8] Reports such as Hawkin's of crocodiles feigning sorrow for their victims also gave rise to the phrase "crocodile tears," which are "false" tears shed without any real emotion behind them, often with the intention of manipulating or garnering sympathy from some unsuspecting soul.

The Known and Unknown

While the innervation of continuous and irritant tears is fairly well understood, the process that stimulates the production of emotional tears has not been clearly defined. Scientists know that messages which stimulate emotional tear production are carried from the lacrimal nucleus along the seventh cranial nerve to the lacrimal gland, the same route which stimulates production of irritant tears. They also know that psychogenic tears are affected by the limbic system of the brain—often referred to as the "emotional brain"—which is associated with memory, behavior, and emotional responses. The limbic system includes the limbic lobe, the hippocampus, the amygdaloid nucleus and a portion of the hypothalamus. The lacrimal nucleus is thought to be connected to the hypothalamus, which is sometimes called the "emotional switchboard" of the brain. It controls the pituitary gland along with other regulatory functions. The lacrimal nucleus also receives messages from several other areas of the brain: the frontal cortex, associated with thought and consciousness; the basal ganglia, which regulate movement and other processes; and the thalamus, which integrates and relays sensory messages to and from various parts of the brain.

Sympathetic stimulation of the small blood vessels in the lacrimal gland is initiated in the sympathetic center of the thoracic cord after receiving a message from the lacrimal nucleus. It then travels along the cervical sympathetic chain through the superior cervical ganglion and on to the lacrimal gland. Sympathetic stimulation may have an effect on tear secretion by regulating blood flow through the lacrimal gland.[9]

As I mentioned earlier, interruptions in nerve pathways affect the production of tears. Destruction of the parasympathetic nerves causes diminished tearing, but damage to the sympathetic nerves causes little change.[10] Scientists have observed that lesions or nerve blockage in some areas influence the secretion of both irritant and emotional tears; lesions or blockage in other areas affect either irritant or emotional tearing. Topical anesthetic on the cornea and conjunctiva inhibits tearing caused by irritation of the eye surface, but emotional weeping is relatively unaffected by the deadening of the surface of the eye and eyelid. Drug-induced tearing, which acts directly on the lacrimal gland, and tearing due to bright light (retinal dazzle) is not affected by topical anesthesia either. Only irritant tears are inhibited when the ophthalmic branch of the fifth facial nerve is severed; psychogenic tearing is unaffected.[11] Emotional tears may be increased or decreased by lesions of the frontal cortex, the basal ganglia, the thalamus, or the hypothalamus.[12] Such lesions may cause impulsive, unmotivated, excessive weeping or laughter. Emotional weeping is prevented when lesions occur in the pathway between the frontal cortex and the parasympathetic nucleus of the facial nerve, but tearing in response to irritation still occurs.[13] Dr. J. Daniel Nelson, clinical director of the Dry Eye and Tear Research Center at SPRMC, said patients with dry eye syndrome usually first notice a decrease in the amount of their continuous tears followed by the loss of tears in response to strong physical stimuli such as smoke, dust, fumes, etc. The ability to shed emotional tears is usually the last tearing function to decrease or disappear. "Patients who are able to shed emotional tears usually suffer less than those who cannot weep in response to emotion. Some persons with dry eye syndrome report they can alleviate the soreness in their eyes by thinking sad thoughts until tears appear," Nelson said.[14]

It is clear that irritant and emotional tearing are innervated and stimulated differently, but how the lacrimal nucleus receives messages to stimulate tears in response to strong emotion is not clear. We still have much to learn about the neurologic and chemical mechanisms by which the brain controls the emotional tearing process. We hope that research on emotional tears and the lacrimal gland will someday help solve the many mysteries surrounding psychogenic tears and the chemical changes that take place in our brains when we feel strong emotion.

3

Shedding Tears for Science

If you have tears, prepare to shed them now.

Shakespeare
Julius Caesar

In my search for information on emotional tears, I found numerous accounts of studies on reflex (irritant) tears starting with a chemical analysis published by Fourcroy and Vauquelin in 1791.[1] Since that time scientists have measured the chemical properties—salt composition, pH, calcium, proteins, lipids, cholesterol, urea, glucose, Vitamin C, enzyme concentrations, and numerous other substances—in irritant and continuous tears.[2] Physical properties of these tears such as volume and rate of secretion have also been investigated.

Tear Comparison Studies

But I found only one report of research specifically on emotional tears. In 1956 and 1957 Robert Brunish, a biochemist from UCLA, conducted a comparison study of emotional and irritant tears. In his paper he stated that emotional tears were similar to the continuous tears that cover the surface of the cornea without stimulation, and thus he referred to emotional tears as "normal" tears. Brunish also included idiopathic (cause unknown) tears in the same category as emotional and continuous tears. We assume the idiopathic tears were mainly from patients with epiphora, a condition in which the nasolacrimal ducts are obstructed and continuous tears constantly overflow instead of draining unnoticeably into the nose as they normally do.

Brunish observed that even though the volume of tears excreted for emotional and idiopathic reasons was greater than that obtained in response to eye irritants, the "normal" tears, which included emotional tears, had a higher protein concentration than irritant-induced tears. He also found that the distribution of the proteins—lysozyme, globulin, and albumin—was different for the two types of tears.[3] Because Brunish placed idiopathic, continuous, and emotional tears into one group, subsequent research that examined the various types of tears separately failed to substantiate the results of his study.

In 1959 ophthalmologist Ulf Krause published an extensive paper on a study of human tear proteins conducted at the Eye Hospital at the University of Helsinki. Krause examined irritant tears and tears of patients with "such profuse epiphora that stimulation was unnecessary." In his study comparing irritant and epiphora tears, he found the two types of tears to be similar and thus concluded that his study did not corroborate Brunish's findings that irritant-induced tears were different from other tears.[4] Krause never examined emotional tears.

That same year Olive F. Erickson reported that continuous tears, collected by placing a piece of filter paper into the conjunctival sac, gave a protein pattern similar to the irritant tears analyzed by Brunish earlier. Although the tip of the filter paper probably produced some irritation, the conjunctival sac should have also contained continuous tears.[5] Erickson's results were consistent with those reported by Krause, signaling a halt to research comparing emotional and irritant tears. No further research of this type was done until twenty years later when we began our tear study.

Brunish's findings fascinated me. It seemed that a misunderstanding due to inconsistent use of terminology and his placing of emotional, continuous, and epiphora tears in the same group was partially to blame for the difference between his and others' findings. Reinterpretation of the results presented in the three studies indicated that continuous tears, irritant-induced tears, and tears from patients with epiphora are similar in protein distribution and concentration, but all three may differ from emotional tears.

My theory suggests that emotional tears should be different from other tears, and I was eager to begin testing this hypothesis by comparing tears shed when humans feel strong emotion with those shed when the eye is irritated by physical or chemical causes. Since Brunish's research was the only report on emotional tears in the scientific literature, I decided to try to determine the validity of his findings.

The purpose of my study was to ascertain the effects of different stimuli on the composition of tear fluid and to find out if the human lacrimal system is able to concentrate and excrete chemical substances in one or more types of tears. In other words, I wanted to learn if emotional tears and reflex tears are chemically different, and what, if anything, is excreted in both types of tears. Do humans get rid of unhealthy levels of certain substances that build up in response to stress when they shed emotional tears? If they do, what substances are excreted?

Anthropologists and psychologists have offered a variety of hypotheses to explain why humans shed emotional tears, but their proposals do not lend themselves easily to experimental verification and consequently have not been tested. But I felt that, because my biochemical theory of tears was more focused, it would perhaps be more easily tested and verified. So I set as my first task to determine if psychogenic tears differ chemically from other types of tears.

But as I began contemplating what experiments should and could be performed, a number of questions arose: How does one make a person cry for emotional reasons without adversely affecting their psychological state? Is it best to solicit tears only in the laboratory, or is it also feasible to ask the subjects to collect their own tears shed for personal reasons? Will the very idea of shedding tears collected for research turn off the weeping process before it begins? What's the best way to collect tears? Once the tears are collected, can they be stored without altering their composition? What laboratory procedures can be adapted to analyze the miniscule amounts of tears and the substances they contain? With so little known about emotional tears, it was clear to me that we would be entering a virtually unexplored field and would probably face numerous problems.

My Tear Study Begins

Several years passed before I was able to begin research on my psychogenic lacrimation theory. After earning my Ph.D. in biochemistry, I worked as a research specialist in the Department of Laboratory Medicine and Pathology at the University of Minnesota. My research at that time concerned the role of intracellular chemical messengers involved in the action of hormones and other substances.

Not until joining the staff of the St. Paul-Ramsey Medical Center (SPRMC) in 1977 did I find a real opportunity to begin to study tears. If it had not been for the vision and multidisciplinary approach to medical research of Dr. V. B. Tuason, head of the SPRMC Psychiatry Department, my tear research may never have gotten off the ground. After I explained my proposal and ideas for studying psychogenic lacrimation to Dr. Tuason, he recognized the potential value of research on emotional tears and crying and encouraged me to proceed with the study and to apply for grants to conduct the research. He also helped obtain financial assistance to begin the tear study before we received any grant funds. In 1979, the St. Paul-Ramsey Medical Education and Research Foundation (MERF) approved a $4,000 grant to study the "Effects of Different Stimuli on the Chemical Compositon of Tears." The following year they approved a follow-up grant for $9,468, and we also received $1,000 that year from the Margaret H. and James E. Kelley Foundation of St. Paul. These two grants, along with about $2,500 donated by private individuals, enabled us to continue the tear study and begin the adult crying behavior study. Then, in 1981 a MERF research grant of $11,188 financed a study entitled "Biochemical, Physiological, and Psychological Studies of the Role of Psychogenic Lacrimation in Alleviating Emotional Stress."

While these grants are relatively small amounts, they provided an important beginning to our study of the mystery of tears. Dr. Tuason's continued interest and support played an essential role in launching the research.

Two students also played an important role in the initial tear study. Denise DeSota-Johnson began work at the Psychiatry Research Laboratories in 1977 as part of Hamline University's internship program. If she had not joined us during that period, the research may have been postponed, since none of us had time to take on any extra work. She was able to work full-time on the tear study and made it possible to begin the research sooner than we had originally anticipated. When Denise left in 1980, Carrie Ahern took her place as research assistant shortly before receiving a B.S. in biochemistry from the the University of Minnesota. I believe Carrie probably spent as many hours as myself working on the tear and crying research.

Onions and Tearjerkers

In designing the methodology for the tear study, first we determined the techniques we would use to measure protein composition. The next step was to find safe, effective, and as pleasant as possible methods to induce reflex and emotional tears. We tried to think of ways to "turn on the taps of the ocular sprinkler system" (Rick Ratcliff, *Detroit Free Press*) with the least amount of physical and emotional discomfort to the subjects.

We did not want to put anything harmful directly into the eye to induce irritant tears and thus ruled out many of the lacrimators (substances that induce the flow of tears) used to stimulate tears in previous studies. We felt that most of those lacrimators—ammonia, chemicals used in tear gas, menthol crystals, and others—would be too caustic and unpleasant for the subjects. Furthermore, many would probably not be approved by the SPRMC Institutional Review Board, which makes decisions on what is allowed in studies involving human subjects.

We also decided against collecting tears by placing one end of a filter paper strip inside the lower eyelid. This method, often used by ophthalmologists to test a patient's tearing reponse, may cause certain cellular components from the surface of the eye to enter the tears thus altering their composition.

Shakespeare's *The Taming of the Shrew* came to mind, in which a lord offers this advice for a young boy playing a theatrical role as a woman:

And if the boy not have a woman's gift,
To rain a shower of commanded tears,
An onion will do well for such a shift.

Onions were our first choice as irritant-tear producers, since people are familiar with them and therefore may be less apprehensive about their effects. But when we initially tested the tear-producing ability of onions in the lab, they produced only limited success. We were looking for a lacrimator we could depend on, not one which just occasionally did the job. One of my associates remembered hearing that eating large amounts of horseradish would bring tears to anyone's eyes. This idea appealed to us because, if it worked, tears could be stimulated without having to directly irritate the surface of the eye. A University of Minnesota graduate student volunteered to test this method of inducing reflex tears. He heaped a teaspoon with prepared horseradish and bravely gulped down the pungent relish. His lacrimal glands did not respond to the horseradish, but his stomach reacted vehemently. So much for that method of inducing tears.

A culinary expert had told us that horseradish retains its potency until cut or grated. So we decided to test the feasibility of inducing tears by breathing vapors from freshly grated horseradish. When I visited a market in search of a fresh supply, they had none on hand but said they could order as many as I needed. Being a city kid who had never seen horseradish in its natural state and therefore assuming they were about the size of salad radishes, I told the grocer to order a dozen. A few days later the grocer called to say my special order of horseradish had arrived. Instead of the little brown bag I expected, the grocer handed me a box weighing about fifteen pounds and a bill for $11.85. Each of the twelve horseradishes was approximately a foot long with the diameter of a cucumber. At least we would have an ample supply in case they turned out to be just the lacrimator we were looking for.

I decided to test this method of inducing irritant tears myself. As some of the horseradish fumes escaped when the cut-up chunks were noisily grating in the blender, I reminded myself that the experiment I was about to perform was for scientific research. Bracing myself, I removed the blender cover and inhaled deeply. One concentrated whiff of the unbelievably caustic vapors that seemed to explode into the air as I lifted the cover sent me bolting out of the lab. The potent fumes made me see stars and momentarily lose my sense of equilibrium. We crossed horseradish off our list of possible lacrimators. The remaining roots were used for culinary purposes rather than scientific, when several hospital employees took them home to make horseradish relish.

After testing several other lacrimators that also were unacceptable, we returned to the onion with its age-old reputation for bringing on tears. Onions contain a volatile chemical called thiopropanal-S-oxide, which readily escapes into the air when onions are cut or peeled. When the thiopropanal-S-oxide comes in contact with the aqueous tear film on the surface of the eye, a chemical reaction occurs that produces sulfuric acid, usually a very effective lacrimator.

This time we tested several varieties of onions and learned that the U.S. No. 1 white onion is very strong and will usually induce tears. Fresh onions, we discovered, are the most potent, which partially explained why the first onions we experimented with did not consistently cause tearing.

The subjects in the preliminary study were asked to lean over freshly cut onions and inhale deeply with their eyes open for about three minutes. Sometimes the onion vapors caused tears to flow and sometimes they did not. We had better results when we grated the onions in a blender not allowing the vapors to quickly dissipate into a large area. (Maybe we had learned something from the horseradish fiasco after all.) The fumes made eyes burn almost immediately, and most subjects began tearing within a minute after they began inhaling the strong onion vapors.

Shedding tears due to the irritation of onion vapors and most eye irritants is not an act totally without emotions. Anyone who has ever cried over onions knows there is some pain and stress involved when the onion vapors make the eyes burn. While theoretically it may be possible to obtain sufficient irritant tears to examine without causing emotional stress to the subject, at this time we know of no practical way to accomplish this.

Once we established onions grated in a blender as our reflex tear inducer, we had little difficulty obtaining reflex tears for our study. Unfortunately, finding a reliable method to help subjects shed emotional tears was, as we had anticipated, far more complex. Because of parental, peer, and societal pressure, many humans have taught themselves to suppress their emotional tears. Adults and older children often feel crying in public makes them vulnerable and thus only allow themselves to weep in private, if at all. Just how were we going to get psychogenic tears to analyze?

Early in our planning we discussed showing emotional movies, but we originally had hoped to examine tears shed in response to real-life events or personal feelings. No one could think of any discreet way to elicit emotional tears in the lab. We were not about to tell persons that their dog died, collect their tears, then explain we had lied in the name of science. We obviously could not lurk around hospital emergency rooms in hopes of gathering tears of grief from distressed family members. At one time we considered asking subjects to try to collect their own emotional tears outside the laboratory but decided it may be difficult to find subjects willing to collect, label, freeze, and deliver their own tears caused by an emotional event in their lives. In an attempt to find a ready source of tears, I wanted to observe persons who could cry at will. I was also very interested in the techniques persons used to bring on their own tears and had hoped to videotape persons who could intentionally turn on tears. The tapes, along with accounts from the subject, would provide additional information about the crying process.

A Minneapolis theater gave us the name of an actress who was adept at producing "theatrical" tears. She agreed to come to our lab to explain and display her technique. But during several attempts to weep in the lab, her lacrimal glands refused to release tears. Although she had wept easily on stage in front of many audiences, even this professional actress with years of experience at producing theatrical tears experienced performance anxiety when asked to surrender her tears for science. Needless to say, we were not encouraged by this experience.

Several employees at SPRMC said they could usually produce tears by thinking sad thoughts and volunteered to try to shed tears in the lab. But their earnest attempts to shed tears for research were no more successful than the dry-eyed actress. One woman who learned of our attempts to locate persons who could make themselves cry volunteered to donate tears for the study. She was successful where others had failed and was able on several occasions to sit quietly in the lab, think sad thoughts, and begin to cry emotional tears. While this was very helpful, we could not rely on a single individual to supply tears for all of our experiments.

After weighing various alternatives, we came to the conclusion that we could not easily collect tears from real-life situations and that sad movies were the only feasible way to elicit emotions strong enough to produce tears in a reasonably large number of people. While movies appeared to be the best choice, they, too, have many drawbacks. The impact of a normally moving cinema would be lessened with the subjects' awareness of participating in a scientific experiment. Although some may not be intimidated by the surroundings, others who would weep while watching a movie at home or in the anonymity of a dark theater may feel too self-conscious to shed tears in a contrived laboratory atmosphere. Most of us might "dry up" when asked to weep in a formal study, especially with an investigator in the room. Another disadvantage of depending on movies to make people weep is the diversity of emotional responses. What makes one person cry may have absolutely no effect on someone else. In spite of these and other limitations, movies seemed to be the easiest, safest, and most effective way to scientifically induce emotional tears.

We needed to find a satisfactory technique to collect the irritant and emotional tears once they spilled over the subjects' eyelids. Only about 100 microliters (five drops) of tears are shed each time a person's eyes are irritated with onion vapors. During a good, all-out emotional cry, a person may shed a full milliliter or more of tears, but even that amounts to only about .033 fluid ounces—a miniscule quantity of fluid to study. Since tears are usually shed in much smaller amounts, we really couldn't afford to lose much of the precious liquid.

Brunish was the first scientist to specifically examine emotional tears, but he was not the first to collect psychogenic tears. Centuries ago Germanic mourners buried jars of tears shed for soldiers who died in battle. According to historians, Nero collected his tears in a vessel while Rome burned.

Unfortunately, even though we were not the first collectors of tears, we could find no information on how to efficiently collect them. At first we thought we would simply have one of our staff on hand to catch the tears in a test tube. That worked fine with the onion-induced tears, but proved unfeasible with emotional tears, for we soon sensed that the subjects preferred to weep in private. So we looked for a simple, unobtrusive method which would allow them to collect their own tears. An optician and a glass blower helped us design an ingenious invention (or so we thought) which consisted of eyeglass frames with glass cups attached to the bottom of the frames. Only too soon did we learn that our tear-catchers worked only if they were customized to fit the varying facial features of the subjects—a project much too costly for our small budget. Many valuable tears shed by subjects wearing these ill-fitting glasses rolled down cheeks right past the collecting cups. After feeling like shedding a few tears ourselves over the loss of many teardrops, we decided to use the inexpensive but workable method of having the subjects collect their own tears by holding a six-milliliter test tube just below their eyelid.

Finding Weepers

Once we established onions and movies as the basic tear inducers for our study and test tubes as the official tear collectors, the next step was to locate a sizeable group of subjects to shed emotional and reflex tears for us. A portion of the grant money was designated to pay subjects to donate tears. Most subjects received between three and ten dollars (depending on how our funds were holding out) for attempting two tearful cries whether they shed tears or not. About one-third of the subjects volunteered to participate as a favor to us after learning about our limited funds. Several others who learned of the tear study through the media offered to donate their tears.

At first we had trouble finding subjects, so we sought participants through newspaper ads. The first advertisement soliciting subjects ran in the classified section of the *Minnesota Daily,* the University of Minnesota newspaper, on July 17, 1979, under the heading "Will You Cry for Us?" We had no idea what kind of response the ad would bring. The phone started ringing shortly after the newpaper came off the press. And it kept ringing. Within forty-eight hours 110 people had signed up for the study. We withdrew the ad. After that and subsequent ads in the *Daily* and other newspapers, we never again had the problem of finding enough subjects.

Seventy-six females and thirty males donated emotional or irritant tears or both for the initial comparison study. They were all healthy adults with no eye disease, ranging in age from eighteen to sixty years of age. The average age was twenty-eight. As is the case in most psychological studies, the majority of the subjects were women. And not surprisingly, 80% in this particular study were female, since males do not usually shed tears as readily as females and therefore may have been reluctant to participate in a study requesting tears. Of this group of 106, only fourteen shed no tears at all; most shed reflex tears. Interestingly, a few subjects who shed emotional tears did not produce any collectible tears when exposed to onion vapors.

Precautions in Collecting Tears

In establishing standards for the tear comparison study, we took precautions to minimize possible contamination of the tear samples. The subjects were asked to wear no type of cosmetics on their face before coming to the laboratory or amphitheater. The subjects were also instructed to avoid rubbing their eyes before and during the study to prevent any damage to the outer layer of the eye. Even slight irritation could alter the composition of their tears. We ran preliminary tests on some tear samples to detect contamination from the skin and eyelids, to determine whether the concentration of substances in tears became diluted as the volume increased, to rule out the possibility of the presence of certain epithelial components, to examine the effects of freezing the samples, and to find other variables that could distort the final analysis of the tears. We found that our methods did not significantly alter the tear composition so long as we collected at least thirty-five microliters of tears in each sample.

The collected tears were transferred into Teflon vials, tightly sealed, labeled, weighed, frozen, and stored at minus 20°C. Broadcaster Charles Osgood commented on the teardrops stashed in the freezer of the psychiatry lab during a segment covering our tear study on "Universe," a CBS television documentary.

He labels and saves them, putting them in what must be the only tear freezer in the world. Frozen tears, if they existed at all until now, belonged in the realm of poetry, rather than science. But here they are, in a laboratory, to be thawed out and examined under microscopes, and analyzed with chromatographs, to find whatever secrets tears may be keeping.

Test Tubes, Not Popcorn

Although ultimately quite productive, our early attempts to elicit tears with sad movies were unsatisfactory. After showing movies to several groups, we learned that sitting elbow to elbow tended to make some subjects uncomfortable and unable to let the tears flow. We tried to give them a sense of privacy—especially the larger audiences—by making the room as dark as possible and by scattering the subjects in seats throughout the 200-seat amphitheater.

In our quest to find a universal tearjerker, we tried to come up with a list of movies that would elicit strong emotional responses in most of the subjects. Easier said than done. What makes humans feel strong emotion varies considerably. A movie that may cause one person to sob uncontrollably may leave another wondering "What's to cry about?" In the preliminary study we asked the participants to write down the titles of movies they thought were sad; but the list was so diverse that it was not much help. We were trying to find films moving enough to make adults cry in spite of the distraction of trying to collect tears in test tubes.

Our selection of films was limited, since some were unavailable or too expensive to justify renting to test their tear-producing qualities. We experimented with sending the subjects to movie theaters, test tubes in hand, but soon abandoned the idea because of logistic problems.

One of my movie selections, *Sundays and Cybele,* an Academy Award winner for best foreign language film, was among the first movies shown in the tear study. Only 10% of the audience wept during what I considered a very sad, emotional movie. Even though the movie had the necessary qualities for a tearjerker—including close personal relationships that end in death—the tragic ending perhaps came too abruptly and was too shocking to induce tears. One woman said the movie made her more mad than sad. Others told us that the subtitles were distracting and made it difficult to really get involved with the characters in the movie. This film's failure to generate tears prompted us to look at exactly what qualities make up a true tear-inducing movie. We learned that along with a certain degree of sadness, a movie that will cause viewers to reach for a tissue must have a prolonged period of sadness or many sad episodes. Long, drawn out sorrow seems to give the audience more time to empathize and become emotionally involved with the characters and situations.

A movie that consistently drew tears for the study was *The Champ,* a story of an adoring son being raised by his washed-up boxer father. The efforts of the boxer's ex-wife to regain custody of their eight-year-old son prompts the broken down fighter to make an ill-fated comeback to the ring. But the two movies that produced the most tears with over one-half of the subjects crying were based on true stories. *Brian's Song,* a made-for-TV movie about the warm relationship between Brian Piccolo and Gale Sayers drew many tears, particularly from men. The friendship of the two teammates on the Chicago Bears football team ends with Piccolo's death from cancer at the age of twenty-six. The other movie, *All Mine to Give,* is a true saga of a Scottish immigrant couple who die and leave their twelve-year-old son struggling to find homes for his five younger brothers and sisters. This movie eventually moved into top place as the best tearjerker.

Nineteen centuries ago, Horace, the great Roman poet, wrote,

As man laughs with those who laugh,
So he weeps with those that weep;
If thou wish me to weep,
Thou must first shed tears thyself;
Then thy sorrows will touch me.

After noting what made the subjects cry while watching various movies shown in the study, I fully agree with Horace's ancient observation. The audience often cried when the characters in the movie cried, which partially explains why *All Mine to Give* generated the most tears. The cast must have shed gallons during the movie. Everything moves along happily in the first half of the movie, but then the sorrow begins and relentlessly grows worse every minute. First the gruff but kindhearted father dies of diphtheria in his wife's arms. Just when you think this true story can't possibly get any more tragic, the mother contracts typhoid fever. On her death bed she gathers her six children around her and in a feeble voice instructs Bobby, the eldest, to find good homes for the children. Each scene gets progressively sadder as Bobby bravely chokes back his own tears and dutifully tries to carry out his responsibilities as the head of the family before even entering his teens.

"That movie never lets up. It just keeps hitting you over the head again and again," said one subject as she handed in her vial of tears. It was hard to believe there was a dry eye among the subjects when the movie ended, but 30% of the viewers reported shedding no tears. Even though 70% of the subjects reported crying during *All Mine to Give,* only about 50% managed to collect tears in their test tubes.

While Charles Osgood and the CBS crew were covering our tear study for the documentary "Universe," they taped one of our Saturday matinees featuring *All Mine to Give.* The crew set up lights on either side of the small movie screen in the amphitheater directing the light on fifteen tear study volunteers clutching test tubes instead of popcorn and Kleenex. Several of the subjects had agreed to be videotaped during the study.

"The movie might be sad, but I doubt if I can cry on camera," said one subject as she signed the consent forms agreeing to be in the study and volunteering to be filmed by the TV crew. Other volunteers expressed similar reservations about being able to cry with TV cameras focused on them, but all were willing to try. They were pleased to learn that CBS, at my request, planned to film the audience only at the beginning of the movie and then turn the lights off until the movie ended.

In spite of the contrived conditions, most subjects who cried managed to catch at least three teardrops (each teardrop is about twenty microliters) in their test tubes. The largest sample collected was a little over one milliliter (about 50 teardrops). As we had expected, the volume of emotional tears collected was twice that of irritant tears. We still collect both types of tears about four times a month to continue our research.

A Flood of Public Response

One of the most surprising things about our crying research is the tremendous amount of publicity and interest it has generated. Approximately 90% of my time in the Psychiatry Research Laboratories now involves the study of Alzheimer's disease and other dementing illnesses. While our research concerning the role of certain brain enzymes in those diseases receives occasional media coverage, the crying studies have attracted almost continuous world-wide attention. Although we did not solicit publicity, SPRMC prepared a press release to respond to inquiries to help avoid inaccurate statements about the tear study. Within a few days of the "weepers wanted" ad, articles appeared in three Twin Cities newspapers. Radio stations called requesting interviews. Before the week ended, a local TV station did a piece on the study, which included a tape of a tear collection session that was picked up by national networks. A University of Minnesota News Service writer brought the story to the attention of UPI, which distributed the article to over a dozen daily U.S. newspapers and many foreign newspapers from Canada to Australia. Magazine reporters and photographers soon began calling the SPRMC switchboard. Within months articles about the tear study appeared in many major U.S. and several foreign magazines. Our work also made its way into the Sunday newspaper comic section when cartoonist Charles Schulz used the crying study as the subject for a conversation between Snoopy and Woodstock in a "Peanuts" cartoon. CBS's "Universe," ABC's "That's Incredible" and "PM Magazine" ran segments about the tear research, and I was asked to appear on TV talk shows and news programs from coast to coast, including ABC's "Good Morning America" and NBC's "Today Show." At first I tried to accept most of the radio interviews since they did not require travel, but I had to turn down many simply because I was unable to get my work done.

Several authors included our work in their books: Lael Wertenbaker (et al) in *Eye: Window to the World,* Donald J. Crump (editor) in *Your Wonderful Body,* Elaine Morgan in *The Aquatic Ape,* Philip G. Zimbardo in *Psychology and Life,* Savine Weizman and Phyllis Kamm in *About Mourning,* and Aletha Solter in *The Aware Baby.*

Our research even found its way into a best-selling novel, *The Clan of the Cave Bear,* by Jean Auel. The main character, Ayla, is separated as a young child from her Cro-Magnon tribe during an earthquake and found by a Neanderthal family and their clan. Her new family is puzzled and concerned when Ayla sheds emotional tears, since they, not being as highly evolved, have not yet developed the ability to produce tears in response to strong emotion. They feel as much anguish or elation, but do not secrete psychogenic tears. In a letter to Langseth, Auel wrote that she decided to use Ayla's tears as one way to differentiate between the main Cro-Magnon character and her almost, but not-quite-human adoptive tribe, after reading that human newborns normally do not shed tears during their first few weeks and that emotional tears had a different chemical makeup than irritant-induced tears.

For almost six years we have received a steady stream of requests for information about crying not only from the media, but from psychiatrists, psychologists, anthropologists, biologists, sociologists, ophthalmologists, and others in the field of science. We also have received numerous letters from individuals describing their particular problem with crying.

When I was first approached about writing a book about my tear and crying behavior research, I felt it would be better to wait until more research was completed. I changed my mind for two reasons. As is the case with many media reports of scientific research, some of the facts in the coverage of the tear and crying behavior studies were distorted or exaggerated. I estimate the coverage was only about 80% accurate. I gave as many interviews as possible and sent interviewers copies of articles I had written for scientific journals and magazines. Unfortunately, the erroneous information in 20% of the summarized reports often sensationalized our results and inaccurately quoted some of my remarks about tears and crying behavior. So one of the main reasons I agreed to write this book was to present an accurate and comprehensive account of our work. And I also felt there was a need to establish the state of present knowledge (or lack of knowledge) about emotional crying and tears so that others interested in entering the field would recognize that there is a tremendous opportunity to contribute to this new area of research.

4

All Tears Are Not the Same

Science can now distinguish physiologically between reflex tears (stirred, for example, by onions) and emotional tears (arising mainly from grief or joy).

Curt Suplee
Smithsonian

In an area where almost nothing is known, researchers have an infinite choice of what to study first. The importance of the initial phase of research into unexplored fields is not so much *where* scientists begin but *that* they begin.

Since we knew tears contained many proteins and the only previous study of emotional tears involved proteins, I began to test my theory by comparing the general protein concentration and composition of different types of tears. As I mentioned earlier, I was interested in applying improved technology to try to resolve the conflicts in earlier studies regarding the chemical composition of emotional and reflex tears. In the tear comparison study, we attempted to determine (1) if emotional and irritant-induced tears differ in protein concentration, (2) if the concentrations of specific proteins—particularly albumins—are different in emotional and irritant tears as suggested by Brunish, and (3) if there is a difference in protein concentration between men's and women's tears.

Tear Proteins' Functions

Specific proteins in tears serve functions such as control of infectious agents, detoxification, regulation of pH and rates of chemical reactions, metal transport, and nourishment of the cornea. Scientists know that the concentrations of certain proteins either increase or decrease in response to mild trauma such as rubbing the eyes, inflammation, or other irritations.[1]

A Dutch tear researcher, Nicholaas J. van Haeringen, has shown that certain enzymes (proteins which act as catalysts) in tears originate in different glands. Some, including lysozyme and amylase, originate only in the main lacrimal gland; others are produced by both the main and accessory glands, and some are produced only by the accessory glands.[2]

Tears contain five major protein groups—prealbumin, albumin, immune globulin, metal-carrying proteins, and lysozyme—along with several minor groups of proteins. Tear prealbumin, a specific albumin, makes up about one-third of the total tear protein and is not found in other body secretions. One function of this negatively-charged protein appears to be to enhance the bacteria-fighting action of another tear protein called lysozyme. Prealbumin apparently neutralizes the positive surface of the bacteria, which makes it easier for lysozyme to destroy the bacteria.[3]

Albumins—identical to blood serum albumins which transport many substances—are present in small amounts in continuous tears and increase markedly in response to mild trauma and irritants.

Four percent of the protein in tears consists of immunoglobulins (Ig), a group of globulins synthesized by lymphocytes and plasma cells which act as antibodies. The levels of two classes of immunoglobulins, IgA and IgG, which constitute most of the tear immunoglobulins, rise during irritant tearing.

Metal-carrying proteins in tears include iron-carrying lactoferrin and copper-carrying ceruloplasmin. The latter is a potent oxidizing agent and may play a role in detoxification activity.

In 1922 Alexander Fleming first discovered tear lysozyme, an antibacterial enzyme that comprises 25% of tear protein. The concentration of this enzyme, also found in saliva and other body fluids, greatly exceeds that found in serum by one-thousand to one, presumably to protect the delicate surface of the eye.[4] In 1950 Ellen Regan linked lysozyme with stress when she reported that the lysozyme content in the colon may increase with painful psychic stimuli.[5]

Important Variables

As we planned our research procedures to compare the concentration and distribution of protein in different types of tears, we tried to assess the many variables not considered in earlier studies. Four variables I felt were particularly important were (1) potential differences that occur as the volume of tears increases, (2) differences among individuals' tear chemistry, (3) differences in the chemistry of an individual's tears on different days, and (4) differences in tears from each eye in the same subject. Researchers have presented evidence that the protein concentration of tears normally in the conjunctival sac is diluted by tear fluid of low protein concentration secreted from the lacrimal gland when the eyes are irritated. They found a steady decrease in the protein concentration until the volume of tears reached about thirty-five microliters. In other words, when the eyes are irritated the protein concentration of continuous tears is diluted by tears from the main lacrimal gland until a certain volume is reached. The data indicates no further effect of increasing tear volume above thirty-five microliters. We thus used no tear samples in our study which were less than thirty-five microliters to avoid the volume-dependent changes in protein concentration.[6]

If tears from the right and left eyes in the same person were different, we would have had to collect emotional and irritant tears from the same eye in our paired samples. Fortunately, we found no significant difference in tears from different eyes in the same subject in our preliminary study. We also found that the differences in irritant tears from the same subject on different days were not large enough to significantly alter our basic conclusions.

In order to eliminate the influence of age, variations in body chemistry, and numerous other factors, we compared the protein concentrations of emotional and irritant-induced tears both obtained from each of twenty-five females and four males.

Our Method

Proteins differ in the intensity of their electrical charge, making it possible to identify groups of proteins according to the magnitude of their positive or negative charge. Brunish reported that the distribution of protein between the lysozyme, albumin, and globulin fractions was different in emotional and irritant tears. He also demonstrated that emotional tears contain twice as much protein in the albumin fraction as that found in irritant tears.[7] In an attempt to verify his results, we separated and measured proteins according to their electrical charge. Contrary to Brunish's findings, we found no differences between the percentage of proteins in irritant and emotional tears that migrate as albumin or any other charged species. In twenty paired samples from twenty men and women, we also found no significant difference in distribution of positively and negatively charged proteins between tears from men and women. Our failure to observe differences in protein patterns of emotional and irritant tears does not prove differences do not exist in individual proteins. Very small or very large protein molecules may not be detected with the method we used. In the future we hope to have funds to examine tears using the more efficient two-dimensional electrophoresis which enables a more detailed analysis of tear proteins. Perhaps another reason we could not confirm Brunish's protein distribution report is that he used paper electrophoresis, and we used more modern methods—each of which have their inadequacies.

The Bradford method, used in our study to determine the protein concentration of human tear samples, is more accurate than the method used in Brunish's 1956 study. In our studies, a chemical dye was mixed with the tear solution, then viewed through a spectrophotometer, which measures the light absorbed by the protein-dye complex. The greater the protein concentration, the higher the absorption of the dye. Each sample of emotional and irritant tears was examined three times to insure a reasonably accurate measurement of protein concentration in each sample.

Our Findings

When we compared emotional tears from forty-two female subjects with irritant tears from sixty-one female subjects, we found *the protein concentration of emotional tears was 21% higher.* The probability of this difference being just due to chance is less than one in one thousand.

Our comparison of the protein concentration in emotional and irritant tears, both obtained from each of twenty-five females and four males showed *the protein concentration of their emotional tears was 24% greater than that of their irritant tears.* The probability that this was due to chance is less than one in one hundred. We found a higher protein concentration for emotional tears from men as well, although we obtained paired samples from only four subjects. No difference in male and female tears was detected when the same stimulus (movie or onion) was used. The protein concentration of emotional tears exceeded that of irritant tears in twenty-three of the twenty-nine paired subjects.

The two primary conclusions from the results of our tear comparison study were (1) that *the lacrimal glands do excrete different types of tears in response to different stimuli,* and (2) that *in spite of the greater volume of emotional tears, they have a higher concentration of protein than irritant tears.* We have yet to learn how and why tears evoked by movies contain a higher protein concentration than those brought forth by onion vapors, but we do know that something truly unique happens when we shed emotional tears. Our study has been confirmed by a recent unpublished study by Hungarian tear researcher István Tapasztó. He informed me that he had found that emotional tears have a 20% higher concentration of protein than irritant tears.[8]

Since Brunish, Tapaztsó, and I all found higher protein concentrations in emotional tears, I feel this line of research should be continued to try to identify specific protein species, which are greatly increased in concentration or are found exclusively in emotional tears. Such studies, along with further work to determine where tear proteins originate, may lead to a better understanding of why humans shed tears in response to stress.

As discussed earlier, the lacrimal glands have the ability to selectively filter certain substances from the blood. The finding that emotional and irritant tears are chemically different is consistent with my theory that our tears remove substances released during stress.[9] However, this does not prove my theory to be correct. First we must demonstrate the presence of significant amounts of chemicals related to emotional stress in emotional tears. Identifying the type and origin of not only proteins but also hormones, neurotransmitters, and other substances specifically elevated in emotional tears, will help us to understand the biochemical basis of emotion and stress.

5

Chemicals in Tears

The beautiful, complex interactions within the brain can be upset by the tiniest chemical changes—changes caused by emotions, environmental pressures, and stress.

George Cage
The Brain[1]

Our most recent research focuses on neurotransmitters (chemical messengers that convey nerve impulses) and hormones in human tears and the lacrimal gland. While the anatomy and innervation of the lacrimal gland is relatively well understood, almost nothing is known about the hormonal regulation of human tear production. Our research on hormones and other substances in tears and the lacrimal gland will improve our understanding of lacrimation and may provide ways to treat physical and emotional tearing disorders.

Dr. Robert Elde, Professor of Anatomy at the University of Minnesota, has used specific methods to determine the presence of hormones and neurotransmitters in the hypothalamus and pituitary gland. Because of his expertise in this area, I approached Dr. Elde and asked him to collaborate on a study of these substances in the human lacrimal gland and tears. Using antibodies which can specifically recognize and identify different hormones and neurotransmitters, he and his assistant, Mary Frick, stained sections of human lacrimal glands (obtained at autopsy by Dr. Daniel Nelson and me) from males ranging in age from thirty-two to eighty-one years of age. Dr. Nelson, head of the ophthalmology department at

SPRMC, had a long-time interest in tearing disorders, especially dry eye syndrome. Sections of the glands were analyzed for different hormones, neurotransmitters, and neuromodulators (substances which affect nerve transmission). Emotional and irritant tear samples obtained from living subjects were also examined.

While many of the tests we ran for various substances produced negative results, the lacrimal gland and tears showed strikingly positive results for three: the hormones prolactin and adrenocorticotropic hormone (ACTH) and the endorphine leucine-enkephalin.

Prolactin

The very name prolactin comes from the ability of this hormone to stimulate lactation and is generally thought of as the hormone that stimulates and sustains milk production in mammals. But this hormone, secreted from the anterior lobe of the pituitary gland, also serves several other functions. It stimulates the development of breast tissue and the formation of the corpus luteum (a glandular body developing in the ovary following ovulation that produces the hormones progesterone and estrogens). Prolactin is also released in response to stress.

Human tears showed very positive staining for prolactin, as did the acinar secretory cells (glandular cells that produce and secrete tears) of the lacrimal gland and the interstitial cells located between the acinar cells in the lacrimal gland. A further study conducted with cell biologist Dennis McGinley indicated that at least part of the prolactin molecule enters the nucleus of the acinar secretory cells. This suggests that perhaps prolactin affects the use of the genetic information (DNA), which determines the structure and function of the lacrimal cells.

While I was trying to understand why prolactin is localized in and around the acinar cells of the lacrimal gland, it occurred to me that perhaps prolactin was capable of binding to receptors on or in the acinar cells. (Receptors are molecules on the surface of or within a cell that recognize and bind with specific molecules, producing some effect on the cell.) This raises the exciting possibility that prolactin may in fact stimulate tear production and excretion.

I think this notion—which at first seems peculiar—may be very reasonable considering how milk production is stimulated. The textbook *Endocrinology of Woman* describes prolactin as the "lactotropic hormone that stimulates milk secretion by acting on the acini of the mammary gland."[2] The concentrated prolactin located in and around the acini of the lacrimal gland certainly does not stimulate milk secretion, but perhaps it plays a role in stimulating tear secretion. Several observations lead me to believe that prolactin may indeed stimulate tear production and the development of the lacrimal gland.

Prolactin levels are high during the first weeks of life and then gradually decrease during the next three months before leveling off.[3] Newborn humans produce continuous and irritant tears from the time of birth, but it takes several days, weeks, or in some cases up to three months before the human infant develops the ability to shed tears in response to emotional stress. Perhaps there is a connection between the final development of the psychogenic lacrimation process and the elevated prolactin levels during the first three months of life.

Male and female infants and children cry about the same amount, but women usually cry more than men. Dr. Janice Hastrup, a psychology professor at the State University of New York-Buffalo, recently conducted a study of adolescent crying and moods involving 160 families, with adolescents as the subjects. According to her study, sex differences in crying frequency appear about age thirteen, with girls maintaining their frequency throughout adolescence and boys showing a sharp decline.[4] Somewhere between the ages of thirteen and sixteen, females develop higher prolactin levels than males.[5] Adult women have serum prolactin levels 50 to 60% higher than adult males.[6] These higher levels may account in part for the fact that women shed tears more often and more readily than men. Perhaps the higher levels of prolactin lower the threshold for tearing. Even if men and women have similar strong emotional reactions to an event, a woman may be more apt to shed tears simply because she has a higher level of prolactin.

Another possible reason for the difference in male and female crying may be due to an anatomical difference in male and female lacrimal glands. Scientists have found a sexual dimorphism (physical difference related to sex) in the lacrimal glands of male and female rats.[7] Lacrimal gland differences between the sexes in humans have yet to be demonstrated. However, glandular differences, perhaps related to hormonal differences between the sexes, may have something to do with the sex differences in crying behavior.

Dry eye syndrome is a major ophthalmic problem often caused by the lacrimal glands not secreting enough tears to keep the surface of the eye moist. Patients must use artificial tears or some other treatment to prevent the surface of their eyes from drying out. Individuals who have trouble with dry eyes have recently formed a support and education group called Moisture Seekers. There is no known cure for this painful, annoying syndrome which occurs more in post-menopausal women than in pre-menopausal women. SPRMC pathologist Erhard Haus and his coworkers recently conducted a study which shows blood plasma prolactin concentrations decrease markedly following menopause.[8]

The discovery of prolactin in the lacrimal gland and tears provides a new direction for research on tear production. Since dry eye symptoms occur more often when prolactin levels are low—such as following menopause and as a side effect of drugs which inhibit prolactin secretion, there may be a connection. Dry eye symptoms have been reported as side effects in three drugs: furosemide, prescribed primarily to reduce water retention; bromocryptine, used to dry up milk secretion, for infertility, and for Parkinson's disease; and clonidine, prescribed for high blood pressure. All three of these drugs inhibit prolactin secretion.[9] We are now studying serum prolactin levels in patients who have dry eye syndrome in an attempt to learn if they have low prolactin levels.

An overabundance of emotional tears can also be a problem. Crying too easily or frequently can be a handicap when it interferes with communication or functioning in general.

Judging from responses in our crying behavior study and letters from and discussions with those who cry very readily, this is not a rare problem. One of our research projects involves measuring the tear and serum prolactin levels in men and women who cry easily and frequently and in those who rarely shed tears.

If the prolactin levels of those who cry frequently are higher than the levels of those who seldom cry, it would suggest that the higher level of prolactin may indeed lower the threshold of crying. This is not to say that a high level of prolactin is the cause of frequent crying, but that with a higher level of prolactin the tears may flow more readily when one feels strong emotion. A person with lower levels of prolactin who experienced the same emotional response may not shed tears. In other words, perhaps prolactin plays a permissive role in the control of crying. It is not clear yet whether the prolactin in the lacrimal gland and tears is made within the gland or is derived from the pituitary gland, which produces and secretes prolactin. If the prolactin is of pituitary origin, perhaps release from the pituitary in response to stress increases the prolactin level in the lacrimal gland and thus reduces our crying threshold.

Levodopa, a drug known to reduce prolactin secretion by the pituitary gland, has recently been reported to be effective in the control of pathological crying by Dr. Fukashi Udaka, a Japanese neurologist, and his coworkers. They describe pathological crying as excessive and inappropriate "crying unrelated to surrounding circumstances or stimulation with no accompanying emotion."[10]

I recently received the following letter from a woman who reported a relationship between her serum prolactin levels and crying. She wrote:

For years I thought I cried a lot just because I am a "sensitive" and "emotional" person. After nearly ten years of no menstrual periods (from age 26 to 35) and various tests, cat scan, etc., I finally agreed to take the drug Parlodel. This drug lowers the prolactin levels so that periods can occur.

As you know, the normal prolactin level is (less than) twenty-five. Mine was 155. I have now been on the drug for six months and my prolactin level is down to forty and I have normal periods.

And my tears have dried up! This is a figure of speech. I still cry sometimes but only with a good reason —because I am upset, hurt, sad, or angry over something specific. I used to cry over something small or large and then not be able to stop. I would cry for hours at a time and cry for days at a time, too.

While this is only anecdotal information, it is consistent with the theory that prolactin plays a role in regulating crying. We are now trying to obtain more detailed information about her health and crying and are seeking other persons who have experienced similar correlations between high serum prolactin (hyperprolactinemia) and excessive crying. We are currently measuring tear and serum prolactin levels in a man with hyperprolactinemia who reported that he cries about twenty-four times a month. This is an unusually high crying frequency for a male.

Further evidence that prolactin possibly stimulates tear production comes from M. Peaker's work with eider ducks which live along seacoasts. In 1970 he reported that injections of prolactin increased the secretions of the supraorbital salt gland—similar in location, innervation, and histology to the human lacrimal gland—in those marine ducks.[11] Also, D. M. Ensor and his coworkers have reported that the circadian (24-hour) pattern of prolactin levels parallels salt gland secretion in a species of marine duck.[12] Their research suggesting the regulation of the avian salt gland by prolactin reinforces my theory that prolactin may play a similar role in the human lacrimal gland.

ACTH

We also found another pituitary hormone, ACTH, in human lacrimal glands. ACTH released from the pituitary gland is recognized as the most reliable indicator of stress. Unlike prolactin, which is located in and around the lacrimal secretory cells, ACTH is primarily present inside the myoepithelial cells that surround the acinar secretory cells. ACTH stimulates the adrenal cortex to secrete its steroid hormones including glucocorticoids, which promote normal metabolism, decrease swelling, and help resist stress. A chemical called corticotropin releasing factor (CRF), produced primarily by the hypothalamus, is thought to control the pituitary gland's release of ACTH.[13] The stimulatory effect of ACTH on the adrenal gland led me to propose at a conference of the International Tear Film Symposium in 1984 that ACTH may also function to stimulate tear secretion in the human lacrimal gland. Following the conference, Michelle Cripps, a biologist from the University of New Orleans, told me about a paper she had seen in the *European Journal of Biochemistry* by Reinhard Jahn and his coworkers. In this 1982 study it was shown that ACTH added to rat lacrimal glands in vitro induced secretion.[14] The authors did not know if their findings had any physiological significance since at that time ACTH had not been found to occur naturally in the lacrimal gland. In addition to our discovery of ACTH in the lacrimal gland, we also found ACTH in human tears and subsequently measured its concentration in thirty-two emotional and sixteen irritant tear samples in collaboration with Barry M. Bernfeld, a California psychologist. Our finding that ACTH is naturally present in human tears and the lacrimal gland along with the results of Jahn's 1982 study suggests that ACTH may play a role in promoting tear secretion. The discovery of the stimulatory hormones prolactin and ACTH in the lacrimal gland and tears may be the first step in finding a treatment not only for dry eye syndrome but also for those who have an overabundance of tears and a decreased threshold for crying.

In the 1950s scientists actively began to study the relationship between brain function and behavior. This was the beginning of the growing field of biological psychiatry. Much research conducted in this field centers around the role of specific chemical messengers in the brain called neurotransmitters. Neurons (nerve cells) are separated by gaps called synapses. Neurotransmitters are small molecules that carry impulses from one neuron to another across the synapses and thus enable brain cells to communicate with one another and with other organs. Researchers have identified more than twenty neurotransmitters that convey messages from one neuron to another. Three of these—norepinephrine, serotonin, and dopamine—belong in the chemical family called amines and are being studied for their role in psychiatric and neurological disorders.

Research to learn more about the body's naturally occurring substances that reduce pain has also increased in recent decades. Since the group of chemicals called opiates such as codeine, morphine, and heroin was so effective in reducing pain and producing a state of euphoria, scientists theorized that the opiates must be binding with a receptor in our bodies. If that were the case, they concluded, then our bodies must produce a substance similar to the opiates. Researchers began looking for naturally occurring opiates. They found several, including beta-endorphine (a large peptide) and leucine-enkephalin and methionine-enkephalin (both pentapeptides almost identical except for one amino acid).

Leucine-Enkephalin

The lacrimal glands we examined stained very positively for leucine-enkephalin, previously thought to occur only in the central nervous system and adrenal medulla. A preliminary study also revealed both emotional and irritant tears contain leucine-enkephalin. This substance is part of the family of brain chemicals known as endorphines, which are thought to modulate pain sensation. Leucine-enkephalin may function in the brain as a neuromodulator (a substance that affects nerve transmission) and may affect pain sensation through its effects on neurons that utilize substance P, a peptide which may transmit pain and itching sensations. In the lacrimal gland, leucine-enkephalin may also function to modulate substance P nerve fibers. Substance P has been previously shown to promote secretion of other exocrine glands.[15] Finnish scientists recently found substance P in nerve fibers around the ducts of the lacrimal glands of rats and guinea pigs.[16] Other studies indicate that enkephalins may modulate stress-induced changes in the immune system and neural responses to mood, anxiety, and seizures.[17]

Leucine-enkephalin occurs primarily in the epithelial cells lining the tear ducts of the lacrimal gland. Thus leucine-enkephalin is located near and may modulate the substance P nerve fibers that may promote secretion of the lacrimal gland. It seems that once formed, leucine-enkephalin is excreted through the adjacent ducts in tears produced by the lacrimal glands in response to both emotional stress and eye irritation.

What else could leucine-enkephalin be doing in the lacrimal gland and tears? There are no known opiate receptors on the surface of the eye or on the nasal mucosa, where a portion of the tears drain through the nasolacrimal ducts. If opiate receptors are found on the surface of the eye and nasal mucosa, perhaps the process of the secretion of leucine-enkephalin by the lacrimal gland, excreted in tears and binding with receptors, serves as some form of self-medication to alter our emotional state. It is also not known how much of the tear's leucine-enkephalin can enter the blood after absorption by the nasal mucosa much as cocaine is absorbed when sniffed.

We have also attempted to measure catecholamines—any of various amines such as epinephrine, norephinephrine, and dopamine that function as hormones or neurotransmitters—in tears. An enzyme that breaks down catecholamines called monoamine oxidase was found in the acinar cells of the human lacrimal gland by a Japanese scientist.[18] Thus far, we have *detected* catecholamines in tears using a radio-enzymatic assay, but we feel this method is inadequate for *measuring* them. Consequently, we are developing new methods to assess tear levels of catecholamines, and how the levels vary with changes in emotional states.

In an article I wrote for *Psychology Today* in January 1980, I discussed our intention to examine tears for chemicals known to be associated with stress. Specifically mentioned were beta-endorphine, ACTH, prolactin, and catecholamines. At that time we had no way of knowing we would actually find some of these substances in tears and in the lacrimal gland. Now the next step is to try to measure the amounts of these substances and to look for other chemicals related to stress.

Manganese

Manganese was another substance we examined in tears and serum. Interest in research on the neurotoxic effects of manganese has increased in recent years because of its use in the production of metal products and also because of the increased discharge of manganese into the air in automobile exhaust. Lead compounds are being replaced by manganese-containing chemicals as anti-knock additives in gasoline.

In the human body, the element manganese is a metal often present as a positively charged ion that participates with enzymes in regulating rates of chemical reactions in the body. Some researchers suggest that manganese may indirectly control neurotransmitter synthesis and that an excess of manganese disrupts this process.[19] While acute toxic effects rarely occur due to ingested manganese, prolonged exposure to manganese dust initially causes bizarre behavior.

For example, in a study of men who work in manganese mines in Chile, scientists report that the miners develop a hypomanic condition (a mania of moderate severity) called locura manganica after prolonged exposure to manganese dust.[20] These early psychiatric symptoms of manganese poisoning are sometimes referred to as manganese mania, which may include mental excitement, aggressive behavior, incoherent talk, impaired judgment, inability to concentrate, and weak memory.[21] This is followed by a neurological phase which produces some symptoms similar to paralysis agitans, a slow form of Parkinson's disease characterized by muscle tremors and weakness, spastic gait, and other signs of neural degeneration.[22]

In an article published in *Ophthalmology Clinics* in 1973, István Tapasztó reported human tears contained remarkably high levels of manganese—5,000 to 10,000 times greater than that known to occur in human blood serum. Male tears, according to his research, contained twenty-four times more manganese than female tears.[23]

After learning that very high concentrations of manganese cause alterations in moods, I became interested in conducting research to verify Tapasztó's results. If manganese concentrations in tears are in fact much higher than in serum, then the lacrimal system may be able to remove and concentrate substances from the blood. This, of course, would add credence to my theory that tears excrete substances from our bodies. I also wanted to find out if the manganese concentrations differed in emotional and irritant tears. Tapasztó did not mention how the tears for his study were stimulated.

We examined the manganese concentration of serum, emotional tears, and irritant tears from fifteen female subjects between the ages of nineteen and fifty-six years. Their average age was twenty-eight. Irritant tears and serum from fourteen males between nineteen and forty years old (also with an average age of twenty-eight) were also analyzed. We used every precaution to minimize contamination in our tear samples, since contamination may have been a factor in the unusually high tear manganese levels found in Tapasztó's study.

Since measurement of tear manganese concentration required specialized equipment not available at SPRMC at the time, we sent our samples to Dr. John McCall, director of the Mayo Medical Center Metals and Toxicology Laboratories in Rochester, Minnesota. Their analysis of serum and tear samples showed the overall manganese concentration in both irritant and emotional tears to be thirty times greater (rather than 5,000 to 10,000) than that of serum from the same subject. Contrary to Tapasztó's report, we detected no significant differences between male and female tears. The manganese concentration of the irritant and emotional tears of the paired samples from the female subjects were similiar.

Despite the quantitative differences in the two studies, they both concluded that the concentration of manganese in tears is substantially higher than in serum. We do not know why tears contain thirty times more manganese than serum. Regardless of the reason for its presence in tears, the great difference between the manganese concentration in tears and serum demonstrates that *the lacrimal gland does concentrate and excrete manganese.*

Since manganese is an element, this rules out the possibility that it is synthesized in the lacrimal gland. Instead, the lacrimal gland must remove and concentrate manganese from the blood or some other source. The unusual ability of this small gland was quite surprising. Even though the mechanism by which manganese is concentrated in tears is unknown, our analyses clearly show that the lacrimal gland—like the avian salt gland—has the ability to remove substances from the body in spite of its lack of kidney structure.

Help for Abnormal Tearing

While our research examining tears for chemicals related to stress and behavioral changes is still in its infancy, I feel we are headed in the right direction. This line of research may someday lead to treatment for the many persons who suffer the pain of burning eyes due to an inadequate tear film.[24] Our results suggest that a person's body chemistry may play a role in establishing one's crying threshold. Thus, further studies on tears may help those who feel handicapped by either crying too readily or not at all. Besides providing a better understanding of the lacrimation process, the study of emotional tears will, I feel, shed light on the biochemical basis of stress that may eventually lead to better methods of preventing and treating emotional, behavioral, and psychological disorders.

6

Investigating Adult Crying Behavior

Life is like an onion. You peel it off one layer at a time, and sometimes you weep.

Carl Sandburg

In conjunction with the tear study, we began an extensive study of adult crying behavior—the most comprehensive study ever done on emotional crying behavior in adults. Originally, I had hoped to do more with the tear comparison study before beginning the behavior study, but I soon realized the expense of analyzing the tears would delay most of the tear research until we obtained more funds. The behavior study, by comparison, was relatively inexpensive, so we began working on it while seeking the additional funds for tear analysis.

Searching for Data

In studying any behavior, it is important to know how that behavior varies in the population. If we are to fully understand the emotional crying process, we must be able to identify both normal and potentially abnormal crying behavior. I spent many hours in libraries trying to find some good data on human crying behavior. Researchers had conducted many studies of infant crying patterns: frequency, vocal sounds, accompanying movements, differences between normal and abnormal infants, using cries in diagnosis, and numerous other aspects of infant crying. However, there had been no real attempt to scientifically define some of the most basic aspects of adult crying behavior. The longer I looked, the more questions I had. How often do adults cry? Once a week? Twice a month? Several times a year? Do men actually cry much less than women, or do they cry mainly in private? How many people never shed tears in response to strong emotion? Do people cry more often at a certain time of day? How does the menstrual cycle affect crying behavior? Are some people genetically predisposed to cry easily or not at all? Do people with certain personality traits cry more or less than others? Do we cry more or less as we grow older?

I was also interested in research on crying behavior of depressed individuals. Rating scales designed to determine the severity of depression experienced by a person usually include items about crying behavior. But once again, I could find no studies which showed that persons suffering from depression cried more or less than persons who were not depressed. This is not surprising, since crying frequency had not even been reported for the normal population. I wanted to know whether depressed individuals actually showed altered crying behavior—as its inclusion in most depression rating scales would suggest.

Biomedical and psychological researchers have written many volumes about numerous aspects of all other excretory functions including urinating, defecating, and exhaling; but I found only one scientific paper devoted to adult crying behavior. In 1972 Dalbir Bindra surveyed twenty-five male and twenty-five female students at McGill University in Montreal. The subjects filled out a questionnaire that asked them to describe one recent (within a month) crying episode and comment generally on their "typical" crying episodes. Bindra described the various forms of weeping—throat lump, watery eyes, flowing tears, sobbing, and blubbering; and he categorized the incidents along with the emotional and physical states which initiated the weeping episodes.[1]

Although studies based on self-reported, retrospective surveys such as Bindra's questionnaire shed some light on a subject, the results are often not very accurate. Research methodology has shown that unless the specific observations of an incident involving human behavior are recorded when or shortly after they occur, the information is almost always unintentionally distorted. Even though the subjects earnestly try to correctly record their experience, the facts are often altered or simply forgotten if too much time elapses between an incident and the time it is recorded.

Since so little data was available on adult crying behavior, I decided to conduct the first study of adult crying frequency. I also wanted to examine how, when, and why adults cry to help establish a clear picture of what constitutes human crying behavior.

Questionnaire and Diary

After consulting with several psychiatrists and psychologists, I drafted a questionnaire and diary, which were used for most of the study. In an attempt to make our study of adult crying behavior as accurate as possible, we asked all subjects to record and describe the specific details of every crying episode in their diary. This was to be done immediately after or as soon as possible after they cried and to continue for a thirty-day period. Every time the subjects cried they entered the date and time; the type of tears (emotional, irritant, or other such as yawning); the situation and thoughts that prompted their crying; how long they cried; a description of the physical characteristics of the episode (lump in throat, watery eyes, flowing tears, sobbing, body movements such as writhing or pacing); and a rating and description of their emotional state before and after crying. Although information reported by the subjects is included in most of the following chapters, great care has been taken to insure anonymity. However, in order to give you a clear idea of how the study was conducted, we asked for and received permission from one subject to use portions of her questionnaire and entire diary as examples in this book. A few details were slightly altered to preserve her anonymity.

QUESTIONNAIRE 1

How many times a month, on the average, do you shed tears because of emotional stress?

10 -20

Were you under any unusual emotional stress during the last month? Please describe. (Refers to month that you recorded crying episodes.)

No

Do you generally feel better, worse, or no different after you have cried? When do you feel better or worse?

Better - shortly after

How do you feel about emotional crying?

I feel it's a good release—especially in private – but it's embarrassing to cry in public because it's usually misunderstood.

Can you stop yourself from shedding emotional tears if you wish?

Not very often

Can you make yourself cry with no external cause? If so, how do you do it?

Sometimes – Think about a family situation that's hurting a member of our family

How do you think others feel when you cry?

Usually embarrassed or superior or defenseless or angry or pity or uncomfortable

How do you feel when someone else cries?

Usually empathy, although at times (even though I am a crier) I feel the ways described in previous question

Any other comments or opinions?

My mother was (and still is) unable to verbally express most feelings and often had tears in her eyes - which she tried to hide - while my sister and I were growing up. I've often wondered if my abundance of tears is a learned response to feelings that I picked up from my mother.

CRYING DIARY

DATE TIME	TYPES OF TEARS			REASON FOR CRYING		DURATION	COMPONENTS OF CRYING EPISODES					RATE INTENSITY (Scale 0-100) EMOTIONS IMMEDIATELY	
	EMOTIONAL TEARS	IRRITANT TEARS (onions, etc.)	OTHER TEARS	SITUATION	THOUGHTS	MINUTES	LUMP IN THROAT	WATERY EYES	FLOWING TEARS	SOBBING	BODY MOVEMENTS	BEFORE CRYING	AFTER CRYING
4/15 3 p.m.	✓			Frustration- could not accomplish anything due to interruptions	Regret not being able to keep up	2-3			✓			Angry 10 Overwhelmed 100 Exhausted 50	Angry 0 Overwhelmed 10 Exhausted 30
4/17 8:15 p.m.	✓			TV show	Dog's Master hurt	1-2		✓				Sympathetic 50 Sad 30	Sympathetic 10 Sad 10 Embarrassed 20
4/18 4:10 p.m.		✓		Peeling onions	"Damn onions"	3-4			✓			—	—
4/19 11:45 a.m.	✓			Easter Church service	Moved by song sung every Easter	1-2		✓				Sentimental 50 Happy 50	10 50
4/21 9:05 a.m.	✓			Discussing painful childhood experience	Why do those things still bother me?	10	✓	✓	✓		(One eye continued to run for about 8 minutes after I stopped "emotional" crying)	Sad 50 Angry 80	0 10
4/25 6:30 p.m.	✓			Son & girlfriend home for visit. Did not offer to help & I was tired	They are inconsiderate, unappreciative, selfish, etc.	15-20	✓	✓	✓	✓	Entire Body shaking —	Angry 40 Abused 80 Disgusted 30	10 30 10
												Disappointed 90	20 Relaxed 50

CRYING DIARY

DATE TIME	TYPES OF TEARS			REASON FOR CRYING		DURATION	COMPONENTS OF CRYING EPISODES					RATE INTENSITY (Scale 0-100)	
	EMOTIONAL TEARS	IRRITANT TEARS (onions, etc.)	OTHER TEARS	SITUATION	THOUGHTS	MINUTES	LUMP IN THROAT	WATERY EYES	FLOWING TEARS	SOBBING	BODY MOVEMENTS	EMOTIONS BEFORE CRYING	IMMEDIATELY AFTER CRYING
4/26 12:15 p.m.	✓			Someone told me they missed my "touch" at work.	Appreciate their kind remarks.	1-2		✓				Happiness 80	80
5/1 7:10 a.m.	✓		Injury	Bumped my head on the cupboard door	@ ## ≈	1		✓				?	
5/3 9:40 a.m.				Thinking about my need to spend more "quality" time with youngest child		1		✓				Sadness 50 Regret 70	0 10
5/5 1:30 p.m.	✓			Looking at painting	Alive with love and beauty	0-1		✓				Happiness 40	60
5/6 2:20 p.m.	✓			Someone said they missed the newsletter column I used to write at a former job.	Don't cry, dummy.	0-1	✓					Joy 80	80
5/8 9:00 a.m.	✓			Visiting a neighbor who just learned of her husband's death	It's not fair. He's too young. Felt sorry for widow and children.	10			✓	✓	✓	Sympathy 70 Loss 50	40 10

-65-

CRYING DIARY

	TYPES OF TEARS			REASON FOR CRYING		DURATION	COMPONENTS OF CRYING EPISODES						RATE INTENSITY (Scale 0-100)	
DATE TIME	EMOTIONAL TEARS	IRRITANT TEARS (onions, etc.)	OTHER TEARS	SITUATION	THOUGHTS	MINUTES	LUMP IN THROAT	WATERY EYES	FLOWING TEARS	SOBBING	BODY MOVEMENTS	EMOTIONS BEFORE CRYING	EMOTIONS IMMEDIATELY AFTER CRYING
5/9 10 a.m.	✓			Discussing misunderstanding with son	Sorry for our previous lack of communication	5-6	✓	✓	✓			Sympathy 40 Sadness 80	10 10
5/10 5:30 p.m.	✓			Reading comments on Mother's Day card	Lucky to have such great kids.							Happiness 60 Humble? 20	50 10
5/13 1:15 p.m.	✓			Phone call from sister	Old pain of growing up without a father. living with us	3-4	✓	✓	✓			Sad 30 Angry 20	10 10

What Is "Normal"?

The primary purpose of our study was to investigate the range of crying behavior among the normal adult population. It is difficult to identify abnormal behavior without first understanding the range of normal behavior. To assure that our subjects were "normal," we did not include those with any indication of a psychiatric disorder in the normal group. Actually, we were overly conscientious about segregating those with a psychological problem. In addition to separating those individuals from the normal population, I also wanted to determine if persons with depression had altered crying behavior. Despite the lack of research on the crying behavior of depressed individuals, questions about crying are often asked patients when the severity of their depression is being assessed. I wanted to establish a normal range of frequency and duration to compare with the frequency and duration of crying episodes in depressed individuals.

The ideal way to establish which subjects fall into the normal category and which do not is to have each one examined by a psychiatrist and tested by a psychologist, but our research budget did not allow this. Instead, we used the Zung Depression Scale, along with questions taken from the latest Diagnostic Manual of the American Psychiatric Association (DSM-III) interspersed throughout the general questionnaire to help identify subjects experiencing depression and other psychiatric disorders.

I wanted this study to provide information about the normal range of adult crying behavior. Yet I had some concern that our study would draw a high percentage of persons who were concerned because they never cried or cried very often and would volunteer for the study as the first step in seeking help. In an attempt to assess the effects of subject selection on the results of our study, we obtained subjects in several ways and grouped them into the following five subpopulations:

1. University of Minnesota students and employees
   This first group to participate in the study responded to an advertisement in the *Minnesota Daily,* asking for male

and female volunteers (including those who don't cry) and promising five dollars upon completion of the study. Thirty-five females (average age twenty-nine) and ten males (average age twenty-seven) made up this subpopulation.

2. SPRMC employees
I personally extended verbal invitations to the subjects in this group, which consisted of ninety females (average age thirty-six) and five males (average age thirty-four).

3. General population responding to "behavioral study" ad
This group responded to an ad we ran in a Twin Cities newspaper offering a fee for participating in a behavior study. We did not identify the type of research in this ad; we wanted to determine whether knowing the nature of the study attracted individuals with certain types of crying behavior. Before describing the purpose of the study to people who responded to our ad, we asked them a variety of questions including their age and crying habits. This group was slightly younger than the others, with fifty females (average age twenty-four) and nineteen males (average age twenty-eight). About one-third of those who responded to the ad refused to participate when they learned we were conducting a crying study.

4. Identical and fraternal twins
We were interested in learning whether genetics played a role in human crying patterns. Do genes affect how often we cry? Dr. David Lykken, a University of Minnesota professor of Psychiatry and Psychology, known for his extensive studies of twins, contacted about four hundred sets of twins inviting them to participate in our study. Of those who responded, 158 females and 104 males chose not to complete the detailed crying diary but did answer a question about how often they cried. As is the case in most psychological studies, more identical twins (derived from the same egg) responded than fraternal twins (developed from two separate eggs fertilized at the same time.) Of the ninety-nine pairs of identical twins who responded, twenty-six pairs completed the study, and nine pairs out of

forty-six pairs of fraternal twins who responded finished the study. This subpopulation also included thirty-nine unpaired twins.

5. Unsolicited volunteers
This group contacted us and offered to participate after learning of our study through the media. At first we were a bit suspicious of this group's eagerness to participate. However, the results of this smallest group—twelve females (average age thirty-three) and one twenty-six year old male—were similar to the results obtained from the other four subpopulations.

Each of the five subpopulations was divided into two groups: those who met all the psychiatric status criteria and those who failed to meet one or more. To be included in the normal group in our study, the subjects had to meet *all six* of the following psychiatric status criteria: (1) no diagnosed psychiatric illness, (2) no medication for psychiatric illness, (3) no mental health counseling during the six months before the study, (4) no evidence of depression lasting at least a week during the six months prior to the study, (5) no evidence of depression as indicated by the Zung Depression Scale, and (6) no evidence of personality disorders.

Thirty-eight percent of the 331 subjects failed to meet one or more of the criteria and were described separately in the study. The other sixty-two percent met all six psychiatric criteria and constituted the normal population in the study.

As noted earlier, some of the subjects who failed to meet all six criteria may have been found to be quite normal with more extensive testing. However, in order to make our normal population as free of individuals with a psychiatric or psychological disorder as possible, we were willing to eliminate certain subjects if we felt uncertain about their psychiatric status.

Population Profile

Overall, 286 female and forty-five male subjects, ranging in age from eighteen to seventy-five years (average age thirty), completed the crying behavior study. In addition, we received estimates of crying frequency from 201 females and 124 males who were either unwilling to take on the task of writing down every crying episode for a thirty-day period or who failed to complete the diary. The results from those who estimated information about their crying behavior were not significantly different from those who completed the study.

The subjects were primarily white Minnesotans with a variety of education levels and occupations. Although each of the five subpopulations differed in demographics and method of selection, the average crying frequency and average length of crying episodes did not differ significantly among the five groups. The forty-three female and twenty male subjects who responded to the ad for a "behavioral study" with no mention of crying, but who either chose not to participate or failed to complete the study, did answer questions about their estimated crying frequency. There was no significant difference between the crying frequency of those individuals and that of the paid subjects who completed the study. No significant correlation between the age of the subjects and crying frequency or episode duration was found in the study. Consequently, I feel the results of our study reasonably represent adult crying behavior in the Twin Cities and outstate Minnesota population from which these subjects were mainly derived.

While we accurately predicted some of the study's results, included in the following chapters, we were very surprised by other findings and the diverse reasons that cause humans to shed emotional tears. We were impressed with the candid responses—some succinct, others quite detailed—that provide many new insights into why adults cry.

7

How, When, and Why Adults Cry

Tears are sometimes as weighty as words.
                                                                    Ovid

In studies that depend on the recording of incidents over an extended period of time, the subjects often start out faithful, but as time goes on, even those with good intentions often fail to finish the project. So we were pleased that the subjects who completed our study diligently recorded information about their crying episodes in the diaries. As a follow up, we interviewed many subjects and tried to make it easy for them to admit they had forgotten to enter at least one episode, but they all insisted they had recorded all their crying episodes.

Frequency and Duration

The gargantuan task of coding and entering the data from the questionnaires and diaries into our computer was done by Carrie Ahern over a one-year period of time. We were not surprised when we compiled data from the approximately 1500 crying episodes in the crying diaries and found that women cry more than men. Our study conclusively confirmed the widely-held belief that females do indeed shed more tears, more often than males. In D. G. Williams' 1982 study on weeping and personality and sex differences, his British female subjects also claimed to weep more often with greater intensity than men.[1] Similar results were obtained by William Lombardo and his colleagues in a 1983 study of university students.[2] The women in our study reported crying an average of 5.3 times a month compared to 1.4 for men. Some subjects cried much more than others—one woman reported twenty-nine episodes during the month—which raised the average number of crying episodes per month. The modes (the most frequently reported number of episodes per month) in our study were three episodes for women and none for men.

One of the biggest differences in male and female crying was the number who did not cry at all during the thirty-day recording period. Only 6% of the women shed no tears at all compared to 45% of the men. The average crying frequency of 104 males who did not keep detailed crying diaries but gave an estimate of their monthly crying frequencies was almost identical to the average for male subjects who kept detailed diaries.

According to our study results, normal female adult crying varies considerably, with anywhere from zero to twenty-nine crying episodes a month falling within the range of normal crying behavior for adults. Therefore, whether a woman never cries or cries nearly every day, she would still fall within the normal range of female adult crying frequency. The range of crying frequencies for normal males in our study (zero to seven episodes per month) was more limited; a larger male population should be studied to confirm this range.

Of the 331 subjects, 38%—111 females and 16 males—failed to meet one or more of the psychiatric status criteria listed in Chapter Six. The 111 females in this group reported crying more often than the normal subjects in the study. They averaged 7.1 crying episodes per month, which lasted an average of eleven minutes, compared to the normal group's average of 5.3 episodes with an average duration of six minutes. No significant difference from the normal group was detected in the sixteen male subjects in this group. They reported an average of two crying episodes a month—about the same as the 1.4 episodes in the normal group—with a shorter average duration of four minutes. The males in the normal group reported a mean of six minutes. Twenty-four depressed females are discussed separately in Chapter Nine.

I have spoken with and received letters from at least ten people who cry more than once a day on the average. We are interested in studying these individuals to determine why they cry so frequently.

Even though women cry more often than men, the average length of crying episodes was six minutes for both men and women. While the shortest teary episodes were two seconds for both men and women, the longest female episode of two hours was four times longer than the longest male episode, which lasted thirty minutes. The short episodes usually involved watery eyes only. The average of six minutes per crying session was also substantially raised by a few long episodes. More crying episodes actually lasted about one minute than any other length of time for both men and women. Crying episodes caused by sadness were considerably longer, an average of seven minutes, compared to tears of joy, where episodes averaged about two minutes.

Differences in Crying

The sensation of a "lump in the throat" sometimes precedes or accompanies crying. During a discussion of crying on the "Today Show," Bryant Gumbel said, "I get a big football in my throat. Sometimes the football rises up and melts down and comes out in the form of tears." While a lump in the throat occurred in 50% of the female crying episodes, men reported having a lump in their throats in only 29% of their episodes. (We did not consider a lump in the throat alone without the accompanying tears as a crying episode.)

Not only do men cry four times less often than women, but even when they do cry, their crying is often less obvious. Almost three-fourths of the men's episodes consisted of watery eyes only, in which the tears welled up but did not flow; women reported just watery eyes in 53% of their crying episodes. Thus, tears spilled over the eyelids in almost one-half of the female episodes compared to only 29% of the male episodes. Bindra also found that women are more prone to have flowing tears than men.[3] Sobbing was reported by our subjects in only 14% of the female and 10% of the male crying episodes. Other body movements besides sobbing were reported in 4% of the female episodes. Therefore, men cry less conspicuously, less often, with less flowing tears.

Time of Day

We were surprised to find that while female crying frequency did not vary significantly between 9 A.M. and 7 P.M., there was a dramatic increase between 7 P.M. and 10 P.M. (Because there were so few male crying episodes, we did not categorize them according to the time of day, since the results would be based on too few episodes to be significant. Only female episodes are included in our time of day results.) *Twice* as many female crying episodes occurred per hour during these evening hours as during daytime hours. Part of the reason for the "prime time" tears was because more people watch TV and see more movies during that time. Crying episodes attributed to TV and movies at that time were five times greater than during the daytime hours, when the subjects were at work or otherwise occupied. Crying episodes caused by interpersonal relations (arguments, etc.) almost doubled during the evening hours, when people usually spend more time at home with family and friends. Perhaps another reason for the increase in crying at night is that many people feel more comfortable shedding tears at home either in the presence of family and friends or by themselves.

We learned from the questionnaire portion of our study that many subjects only allow themselves to cry in solitude. Only when no one else is around (which is often during the evening hours) do they permit themselves to shed the tears they have suppressed in the company of others. Fatigue may also lower the crying threshold at night.

Causes

A variety of reasons—all involving some form of emotional stress—were given as the stimuli for tears. Most (40%) of the eight hundred crying episodes reported by women were triggered by interpersonal relations—arguments, weddings, love affairs. Other stimuli were 27% media (TV, movies, reading), 6% sad thoughts, 1% physical pain, and 26% "other."

Men attributed 36% of their crying episodes to TV shows, movies, and books. They also reported that 36% of their teary sessions were caused by interpersonal relations. Sad thoughts were the stimulus for 9% of male crying episodes. The remaining 19% of the episodes were for a variety of reasons. While no men reported crying because of physical pain, a study of a larger population of adult males would probably show that this occasionally occurs.

Not surprisingly, sadness was the primary emotion associated with crying in most male and female episodes, accounting for almost one-half of all crying. The emotion behind the tears in 21% of female crying episodes was attributed to happiness. One in ten episodes involved anger; one in fifteen, sympathy; one in twenty, anxiety; and one in thirty, fear. The subjects rated the intensity of their emotions on a scale of one to one-hundred before and after crying. In crying episodes associated with sadness or anger, the subjects reported an average reduction of emotional intensity of 40%. In other words, they felt 40% less sad or angry after crying. They also reported a reduction of intensity following crying episodes attributed to sympathy, anxiety, and fear. Subjects in Bindra's study reported reduced intensity when weeping begins. This is consistent with our finding that people generally feel better after they cry.

I am frequently asked the following questions: "I cry about ten times a month. Is that normal?"; or "Do you know what could be wrong with my friend? She seems OK, except that she cries almost every day."; or "I only remember seeing my father crying twice in the last ten years. Is that good or bad?" I feel that the most important finding in our study is the wide range of crying frequency in psychologically normal persons. According to the results of our study, women who never shed a single tear as well as those who weep almost daily fall into the normal range of adult crying behavior; so do men who cry from zero to seven times a month. Crying frequently or never crying may, however, affect a person's health. Further research on both extremes of crying frequency is necessary to determine the effects of and reasons for the absence or abundance of tears.

8

Crying and Genes, Personality, Menstruation, and Depression

What we anticipate seldom occurs;
what we least expect generally happens.

Benjamin Disraeli

As part of the crying study, I wanted to examine the effects of genetics, personality, the menstrual cycle, and depression on crying behavior. Although general assumptions about crying behavior in relation to these four categories (particularly personality, the menstrual cycle, and depression) appear in the literature, I found that no specific research had addressed their correlation with actual crying frequency. I felt our study provided an opportunity to begin to collect scientific data to replace the assumptions primarily based on anecdotal evidence. Hopefully, our work in these areas will encourage other researchers to expand our studies to help dispel some generally accepted myths about tears.

Genes

One of the things we tried to determine in our crying study was whether heredity played a role in human crying behavior. If our genes influence the frequency with which we cry, then a pair of identical twins with the same genes should have more similar crying patterns than a pair of fraternal twins who have different genes.

However, when we compared the crying patterns between the twenty-six pairs of identical twins and the nine pairs of fraternal twins who completed our study and also the ninety-nine pairs of identical twins and forty-six pairs of fraternal twins who made crying frequency estimates, we found that the crying frequencies of the identical twins in each pair were no more alike than the crying frequencies of the fraternal twins. Our study thus failed to demonstrate any genetic contribution to crying behavior. We were quite surprised by this result.

A comparison of the crying behavior between the twin group and the other subpopulations also showed no significant difference. We concluded that factors other than genes determine crying frequency differences among members of the same sex. These other factors may include environmental influences such as examples of crying behavior by parents, siblings, and peers along with pressure by these individuals and society in general to adopt certain crying behaviors. Individual differences in hormonal levels may also play a role in determining crying frequency. Finally, life stress and life events certainly have an effect on how often an individual cries.

Personality

We were also interested in learning whether there is any correlation between personality and crying, since it had not been established that certain types of personalities tend to cry more than others. No one knew, for example, if people who feel alienated cry more since they have trouble dealing with an "unkind world," or if people with impulsive tendencies cry more than most because they tend to react spontaneously to situations, or if authoritative individuals cry less in order to maintain their authoritative image. In our study we hoped to answer some basic questions about the influence of personality on crying. Do persons who are socially adept cry less because they experience less stress in dealing with others than someone who is shy or socially inept? Does an achievement-oriented person cry more than someone who cares less about their accomplishments? Do those who are comfortable with intimacy cry more or less than those who tend to be aloof? To determine if the measurable aspects of personality and crying were interrelated, we administered the Differential Personality Questionnaire (DPQ) to about one-third of the subjects. This questionnaire was designed by Dr. Auge Tellegen, a well-known University of Minnesota psychologist and personality researcher.

Sixty-five female subjects completed Dr. Tellegen's Personality Questionnaire, which measures eleven basic personality dimensions: well-being, social potency, achievement, social closeness, stress, alienation, aggression, impulsiveness, danger-seeking, authoritarianism, and absorption (how easily persons become absorbed in fantasy).

When we analyzed the first few DPQ's the results suggested a strong correlation between crying and personality. I felt strongly that we would find some dramatic relationships as we compiled results from more subjects.

Using a different method to measure personality, D. G. Williams found that those subjects who rated high in empathy also reported increased crying frequency. However, after analyzing results on all sixty-five subjects, we found *no* significant correlation between crying frequency and any of the eleven personality scales. In other words, either crying frequency is truly unrelated to personality, or the Differential Personality Questionnaire does not measure that aspect of personality.

Menstruation

Hormones that regulate the menstrual cycle are thought to cause mood changes in some women. Until recently, premenstrual symptoms were often attributed to psychological problems. In fact, the word "uterus" comes from the Greek word for hysteria. Some scientists now attribute the emotional, behavioral, and physical changes in part to an imbalance of the hormones estrogen and progesterone.

In a 1968 study designed to help develop a menstrual distress questionnaire, Stanford University psychiatrist

Rudolph Moos asked 839 women to rate forty-seven symptoms associated with their most recent and their worst menstrual cycles. Crying was listed as a factor in a "negative affect" category along with irritability, mood swings, depression, and tension. Overall, the women estimated that their premenstrual crying increased five times and their crying during menstruation increased four times over their intermenstrual crying.[1]

In the "other comments or opinion" section of the questionnaire, filled out by the subjects in our study, twelve women mentioned they cried easily either before or during menstruation. Six women reported crying easily over "silly nothings" or "things that usually don't bother me" along with a mild depression a few days before the onset of menstruation. The others mentioned often "having a good cry" sometime before or during their period. One woman was puzzled by her tears which usually appeared on the first day of her period. "Why am I crying? I'm not depressed or sad." she wrote.

Until our study, no research recording crying episodes during the menstrual cycle had been conducted. Crying is often associated with premenstrual behavioral and emotional changes in women who do not have symptoms severe enough to be diagnosed as PMS. Some lists describing possible symptoms of PMS include items such as "crying spells."

One of the things we tried to determine in the adult crying behavior study was whether female crying actually fluctuates during the course of the menstrual cycle. The female subjects were asked to record the first day or days of their menstrual cycles that occurred during the month they recorded their crying episodes. We examined the number and length of the crying episodes of eighty-five normal female subjects who were not on birth control or other hormone medication. None of the subjects reported having PMS.

We are deeply grateful to biometrist Bruce Gunderson for his help in analyzing the results of our menstrual cycle research. (Biometry is the application of statistical methods to biological facts.) He accomplished what three computer programmers had failed to do—devise a computer program to statistically analyze the relationship between crying frequency and duration and the individual menstrual cycles.

After examining the number of episodes per subject per day and the number of women crying per day in relation to the menstrual cycle, we found three consistent peaks of crying frequency. Increased crying was observed four to six days before the onset of the menstrual period, three to five days after the onset of menstruation, and thirteen to sixteen days after the onset of menstruation (around ovulation). Surprisingly, crying frequency was quite low during the three days prior to the onset of menstruation—days often considered the most problematic in the premenstrual syndrome. Our data shows women do *not* cry more during this three-day period; that does not mean they do not feel like crying or have other symptoms, only that they cry less during the three days before menstruation begins. However, the peak of crying that occurs four to six days before the onset of menstruation is still within the time usually associated with great premenstrual distress.

We had anticipated detecting a pattern that correlated with changes in one of the sex hormones. We found none. The three peaks of crying do not correlate with levels of any single sex hormone such as progesterone or estrogen.[2]

Depression

Even though crying frequency had not actually been measured in a group of depressed individuals until our study, crying behavior is often considered when rating depression. Most of the scales used to rate and help diagnose depression include at least one item about crying such as: "I have crying spells or feel like it"; "I cry all the time now"; "reports crying spells, cries easily"; or "has a tendency to weep."

Of the group who did not meet the mental health criteria, twenty-four females met our criteria for current depression. (Only females were included in this group, since the male sample with depression was too small to be of any significance.) These twenty-four females reported an average crying frequency of eight episodes per month compared to five episodes in the normal group. Although the depressed group cried significantly more times per month than the normal group, their range of crying frequency was quite similar to the normal group's. Those who indicated current depression cried one to thirty-one times per month compared to zero to twenty-nine times per month for the normal group. The duration of crying episodes in this depressed group was not significantly different from the normal group. This considerable overlap suggests that the usefulness of crying frequency as a diagnostic symptom of depression may be quite limited. More research on the correlation between crying and depression should be done before crying can be considered an indication of depression. Specifically, a study comparing the crying behavior of well-defined depressed with nondepressed psychiatric patients and normal controls is needed. Some psychiatrists have indicated that tears are diagnostic not of depression but of some therapeutic change.

The results of the research discussed in this chapter bring to mind this observation by Thomas Henry Huxley: "The great tragedy of Science—the slaying of a beautiful hypothesis by an ugly fact." Since none of our preconceived notions about crying in relationship to genetics, personality, menstruation, and depression were confirmed in our study, our thinking in this regard had to be altered.

9

Major Causes of Emotional Tears

What poetry there is in human tears!

Heinrich Heine

What specifically moves adults to tears? The results of our study affirm the wisdom of Cervantes' observation in *Don Quixote*: "He loves you well who makes you weep." As discussed earlier, we found that interpersonal relations were responsible for the most crying episodes recorded in the diaries, followed by media (movies, television, etc.), sad thoughts, physical pain, and a variety of other causes. This chapter further categorizes the diverse reasons to which subjects attributed their crying episodes and gives numerous examples of the stimuli for their tears.

Interpersonal Relations

"Relationship *is* life, and this relationship is a constant movement, a constant change," wrote J. Krishnamurti. The main cause of crying episodes (40% of the women's and 36% of the men's) reported by the subjects in the crying study diaries was interpersonal relations with family, friends, and coworkers. Whether an individual felt sorrow because of death, divorce, or other loss, or joy due to an engagement, the birth of a child, an accolade, or other emotions such as dejection, anger, frustration, or sympathy, most of the crying episodes in this category were attributed to some type of change in a relationship. Although some reasons given as the cause of tears in the diaries were duplicates, there were almost as many reasons for crying as there were crying episodes in the interpersonal relations category.

Subjects listed the loss of a special person in their own or others' lives due to death or the termination of a relationship as the cause for over fifty crying episodes. Many persons shed tears at funerals during a "moving eulogy" while thinking of their loss, and the tears of bereavement continued long after the loss.

- Sympathy for another's sorrow drew many subjects' tears. A grieving father wept when he saw his "wife crying over the death of our baby." Several subjects reported shedding tears while "talking to the bereaved" or "consoling a friend" who had lost a loved one. Another subject cried after "seeing the devastating effects on the family of an aunt who died."

- The loss of anticipated motherhood caused one woman to shed tears when she learned her "pregnancy test came back negative." Some women cried on several occasions after suffering miscarriages, and one reported that tears appeared whenever she "read about, heard of, or saw a baby."

- The end of relationships between lovers or spouses also was given as the cause of many crying episodes. Breaking up an engagement, marriage, or strong relationship often brought tears before, during, and after the separation. Subjects wept when

  "Thinking about a relationship that's not going to work out."

  "Divorce papers in the mail."

  "Thinking about my divorce . . . and wishing it could have worked out."

  "Best friend is going out with the girl I love."

- Anticipation of possible loss when they learned of or visited family members or friends who were ill or in pain brought tears to many subjects. Some specific reasons given were

  "Seeing mother in hospital hooked to machines."

  "Watching best friend suffer in hospital."

"Feeling helpless over father's illness."

"Depressed about boyfriend having only a few years to live."

- A sense of relief made one woman cry when she "learned Mom's x-rays showed nothing serious." A mother wept when her "son found out he's exempt from military service."
- Anyone who has lost a cherished pet perhaps has experienced feelings similar to these subjects who wept when

    "Our thirteen-year-old family dog had to be put to sleep."

    "Coming home to an empty house the day after having our dog put to sleep."

- Tearful departures accounted for many episodes with "saying good-bye to boyfriend" and "saying good-bye to friends" listed most often. Other farewells that caused tears involved someone moving out of the home or a long distance away:

    "Leaving home and boyfriend to go to college."

    "Saying good-bye to mother, moving out of state."

    "Splitting up with roommates."

    One woman who did not cry during the month she kept her crying diary added this comment: "I hardly ever cry but couldn't hold back the tears when my adult children (whom I raised alone) left home."

- Wedding arrangements brought tears to several engaged subjects because of "frustration over parent's control of wedding" and the disappointments and hassles involved in the production of a large wedding.
- "Argument with husband" appeared often in the diaries as a reason for women's episodes along with "lack of communication" as expressed by the women who wrote,

    "Can't seem to get through to my husband what's important to me."

    "Our marriage isn't as happy as I'd hoped it would be."

    "Sex was frustrating."

- The chore war was mentioned at least a dozen times as the cause of tears often shed while doing domestic chores:

"Resentful that family didn't help more."

"Sick of doing housework with no help."

"Husband leaving me alone with kids again."

- Exasperation with the demands of motherhood was given as stimuli for some crying episodes:

    "Regret over not enough quality time to spend with each child."

    "Kids demanding too much all at once."

    "Both kids tired and crabby."

    "Frustrated and tired after being home alone with restless kids all day and night."

    "Shattered by verbal attack from teenage daughter."

- Dissatisfaction with parents prompted many episodes such as one man who reported shedding tears while driving home and feeling "sad" after a visit to parent's home. "Felt we hadn't talked enough." Others wept over a lack of understanding by parents or frustration with in-laws:

    "Mad because Dad will not listen to me."

    "Heart-to-heart talk with Mom. She doesn't understand how I feel."

    "Parents insensitive to my feelings. They're always right."

    "Imposing in-laws."

    "Mother-in-law's coming for two-week visit. Can I stand it that long?"

- Problems with coworkers accounted for several incidents with subjects citing reasons such as:

    "Derogatory remarks by staff member at staff meeting."

    "Bossy, mean coworker."

    "Fed up with having to do someone else's job."

    "Yelled at for something that wasn't my fault."

    "Too many people giving me orders."

Even though about fifty crying episodes were work-related, very few subjects cried on the job or in front of others at work. Those episodes that occurred at work were usually very short, and most of the subjects waited until they were alone or at home before allowing their job-related tears to flow freely.

While the majority of the subjects' crying episodes due to interpersonal relations were caused by what are usually considered negative emotions—sadness, anger, and frustration—many subjects reported shedding tears for joy, appreciation, and other pleasurable excitement:

- Subjects gave varied reasons for their "tears of joy."
   "The bride coming down the aisle always brings tears."
   "Seeing their love for each other."
   "Proud of son and others in school orchestra concert."
   "Surprised and happy to receive engagement ring."
- Expressing or just thinking about deep love between a man and a woman had brought tears to some subjects. One woman said she wept when her "boyfriend told me how much he loves me." Several women attributed tears to times when they were "feeling much love for husband." A few reported shedding tears while making love due to "excitement before," "sweetness and goodness prior to orgasm," and "pleasure and fulfillment after."
- Subjects about to become parents or grandparents cried when they heard the news. A new grandmother shed tears when "seeing beautiful grandson for the first time."
- Not all work-related crying episodes had negative overtones such as those mentioned earlier. Appreciation for a job well-done elicited tears. One subject reported being moved to tears when her "supervisor touched my hand while discussing good aspects of my work," and another cried when she was "overwhelmed by positive feedback from supervisor." A subject who evidently works in a supervisory capacity shed tears when she "received a thank-you note for an evaluation."

Some psychoanalysts suggest that all tears are due to sadness and there are no such things as "happy" tears. Sanford Feldman wrote, "There are no tears of joy, only tears of sorrow." He proposes that tears shed in response to happy events or thoughts are actually tears due to delayed or suppressed sadness or guilt which are released when things turn out well. Feldman further suggests, "When something makes us happy, especially when a sad and painful situation turns out well making us joyous and happy, the fundamental knowledge and feeling that this is only temporary and not lasting breaks into our mind and makes us cry."[1] While there may be some rare instances in which tears of joy are intermingled with tears of sadness, I feel that any strong emotion—whether it be elation, rapture, sorrow, or anger—can elicit tears and I definitely believe humans often do shed "tears of joy."

Media Stories

Media stories, true and fictional, ranked a close second to interpersonal relations as the cause of emotional tears in adults. About 250 of the crying episodes in the crying behavior study were attributed to TV shows, movies, plays, books, newspaper and magazine articles, and news reports. Some subjects said they rarely cried *except* while watching TV or a movie. Those subjects who shed tears frequently for personal and other reasons also often wept in response to fictitious or real-life drama on TV or movie screens. Some people actually seek out a sad film when they feel the need to "have a good cry."

Jay Efran and Timothy Spangler, psychologists from Temple University, had hoped to learn the technique that writers use to develop their tear-inducing plots. However, they abandoned the idea after preliminary interviews suggested that authors basically have no technique to induce psychogenic lacrimation, but instead rely on their intuition to tell them what will bring their audience or readers to tears.[2] Evidently Alan Alda, Michael Landon, and other writers of tear-jerking scripts have a sixth sense about what makes humans cry. Robert Frost offered this observation about writers and weeping: "No tears in the author, no tears in the reader." In any case, we learned that the following shows or type of stories succeeded in eliciting tears:

- "M*A*S*H" was the single show which drew the most tears. Two episodes, one about Colonel Potter being far from home on his wedding anniversary and the other in which he gives his horse to an old dying Korean man, were responsible for many tears. Our crying behavior study was completed before the last episode of "M*A*S*H," which was seen by 120 million people. I have often wondered if a record for the most people crying at the same time was set during the last half hour of the final two-hour "M*A*S*H" show. "Little House on the Prairie" and various soap operas were also listed often as the cause of tears.

- Other shows that made viewers weep covered a diverse range, from those with serious subject matter such as "60 Minutes" and "Donahue" to lighter shows such as the "Miss America Pageant" and various game shows.
- Stories in TV, movies, or print that dealt with children drew the most tears in the media category. Watching young people in difficult life situations elicited both sadness and joy as evidenced by the following reasons given by subjects:

    "Little girl separated from her parents."
    "Sorry for black children in an all-white school."
    "Felt sorry for abused child."
    "How could father just walk away from his family?"
    "Touched by courage of handicapped boy."

- "Sorry for parents" was listed often for a variety of reasons —particularly when the story involved sick, injured, or dying children. Other episodes involved parent-child relations:

    "Touching moment between dad and adult son."
    "Nostalgic parting of mother and son."
    "Dad disowns son."

- Man-woman relationships accounted for some viewers' tears, but fewer than we had expected, based on the large number of crying episodes attributed to real male-female relationships reported in the study. Some tears came because the subject felt "sad the couple's love had futile future"; other subjects were moved by a "happy marriage" and the "togetherness of the couple." One person shed tears at a play when he was "touched by the line 'I love you on purpose.'"

- One subject wrote that even though she seldom cries for personal reasons, she often sheds tears during commercials: "I've never been able to decide what I feel when I cry during commercials. I'm just touched by the purity of the moment." Evidently the advertising agencies know how to create moving, tender, nostalgic moments, since other subjects also reported shedding tears during commercials. "Reminds me of home" was the reason one subject gave for her "commercial" tears; another was moved by "sweet, cute, delightful children."

- Tragic news reports were responsible for some episodes:
    "Teenagers killed the day before graduation."
    "Boy with leukemia died."
    "Woman dying of cancer and how her family is
        supporting her."
    "Plight of the poor."
- Sad news involving public figures caused some to cry. John Lennon's death caused tears in several subjects, along with thoughts such as "sense of loss, emptiness." One man wrote: "I seldom cry. The last time was when I heard John Lennon died." Several subjects reported weeping when they learned that President Reagan was struck by a bullet. A few cried during a news clip in which "Mrs. Reagan talked about Ron being shot."
- Abuse of dogs and horses and the slaughter of baby seals and sea lions in the news also brought some to tears.
- Accounts of the human spirit attempting to overcome tremendous hurdles were given as the reason for some episodes. Several wept while watching reports of balloonist Thor Heyerdahl fly into Paris greeted by five thousand Parisians waving American flags. Others cried while watching a "woman trying hard in spite of a handicap" and a "man with one leg determined to play basketball, football, and track."
- "The horrid effects of war" was a typical reason given for crying while watching *The Deer Hunter.* Other movies that elicited tears from subjects were *Miracle on Ice, Elephant Man, Madame X, Tribute, Peege, Ordinary People, Sound of Music, Marjoric Morningstar, The Champ, Love Story, Wizard of Oz, Gone with the Wind, A Little Romance,* and *Romeo and Juliet.* The subject who wept during the final

moments of *Tale of Two Cities* wrote: "Great ending to a great story."

Miscellaneous Stimuli

- Six percent of the episodes in the study were attributed to sad and lonely thoughts triggered by a variety of stimuli. Nine were caused by feeling "lonesome for loved one." Others shed tears while writing Christmas greeting cards and missing the person to whom they were writing. Another subject's tears fell when she "felt lonely and sad on a walk," and several teary sessions were due to feeling "very lonely."
- About fifty episodes were triggered by music—often because the songs reminded the subject of happy or sad moments or produced strong feelings about a person or situation. "The Way We Were" was mentioned most often along with Christmas songs, hymns, and even "The Battle Hymn of the Republic." Others attributed their tears to the sheer beauty of the song, the singer, or the instrumentalist, such as one subject who wept when "listening to a sweet, tiny girl sing a song." During an audition, a concert violinist explained his tears as a gifted young girl played a difficult piece. "Hearing her play is like listening to her soul," he said.
- Of the almost forty episodes which occurred during church services, about one-third involved church music. Some shed tears while "listening to the church choir sing a beautiful, moving song"; others wept while "singing a great old hymn at church." One subject wrote, "Church music always makes me cry." For others, church seems to provide time for meditation and a place where barriers that usually curb feeling and spirituality are relaxed. Tears flowed in church when subjects were "touched by a service" and "feeling close to God"; others shed tears while experiencing overwhelming feelings brought on by sermons or prayers. Reflections and thoughts about life in general during church services prompted tears in eleven subjects. With some persons, church and tears were concomitant, and there

seem to be many persons like the individual who wrote, "I almost always cry in church."

Evidently, "spiritual" tears are not uncommon. The "gift of tears" as part of religious experience was described in detail by Catholic theologian Robert Cardinal Bellarmine in the seventeenth century.[3] And Saint Ignatius Loyola, founder of the Jesuits, is one of many saints who reported copious amounts of such tears. He wrote in his *Spiritual Diary* in 1544, "I had an abundance of tears, without experiencing understandings or distinctions or perceptions of any persons, but accompanied by a most intense love, warmth, and great relish for divine things and an exceedingly deep satisfaction of soul." In one forty-day span, Ignatius mentions tears 175 times, an average of over four times a day.[4] I have received several letters from persons in the Pentecostal Church who wrote that tears frequently accompany their church services and prayers.

- A few subjects reported shedding tears for happy reasons such as "an enjoyable walk on a beautiful day," being "overwhelmed by the beauty of a sunset," and "seeing friend's new art work." Arthur Koestler, author of *The Act of Creation,* refers to such feelings of rapture as "self-transcending emotions" in which "the 'I' seems no longer to exist, to dissolve in the experience like a grain of salt in water; awareness becomes de-personalized and expands into 'the oceanic feelings of limitless extension and oneness with the universe.'" These enraptured, entranced feelings cause a surplus of emotion which "cannot be worked off in action . . [but] can be consummated only in *internal,* visceral, and glandular processes," he wrote in a chapter entitled "The Logic of the Moist Eye."[5]

- One percent of the women's crying episodes were caused by physical pain when they "hit knee on table" or "banged head on cupboard door," or the like. Other pain-related episodes were the result of burns from hot food, boiling water, and overexposure to the sun. "Have the flu, feel awful, hate being sick," wrote one of several subjects who had shed tears due to physical discomfort associated with illness; another episode was attributed to "menstrual cramps."

- Weariness, overwork, and a sense of not keeping up with responsibilities were listed as reasons for about twenty episodes. One can almost feel the fatigue and frustration in some of the following subjects' situations and feelings that brought on tears:

  "Have too much to do. I'll never get done."

  "Tired and frustrated; hoping to relax but came home to much work."

  "Exhausted from working sixteen hours straight."

  "Very busy. Three M.D.'s to one R.N. I can't do it all!!!"

  A gradual build-up of fatigue or frustration was probably the underlying cause of one mother's crying episode, triggered by her son's eating the chocolate chips she had planned to use in cookies. This seemingly trivial event was evidently the last straw for her.

- Discontent at work such as dealing with "rotten job I don't like" or general feelings of "lack of appreciation and compensation" caused some episodes. Others shed tears after "a bad day at the office" or when "everything went wrong at work today."

- Money problems were given as the cause of fourteen crying sessions by subjects who surely must agree with Ogden Nash's observation from "Happy Days":

  Certainly there are lots of things in life
  > that
  money won't buy, but it's very funny—
  have you ever tried to buy them without money?

  Here are some situations that precipitated money-related tears:

  "Check bounced."

  "Wondering if I'll ever find a job or have money."

  "Being broke, having to ask parents for money."

  "Frustration and anger over income tax and welfare."

  "Not enough money to do anything extra."

- Problems and disappointment with aspects of school—difficult homework, anxiety over exams, and professor problems

—prompted about twenty crying episodes. The following are typical reasons given by students:

"Missed an A by one point on a 200-point exam."

"Failed chemistry final."

"Felt like a failure when received letter of rejection from medical school."

"Turned down by graduate program."

"Intimidated by and disappointed with a professor."

- A few persons reported weeping due to fear—fear of bugs, thunder and lightning, and losing a job. Others shed tears after the loss—due to theft or misplacement—of important objects such as a savings passbook, glasses, and a family memento. A woman cried while "discussing being sexually molested." Three persons awoke from bad dreams to find themselves crying. One subject's tears were self-induced while she was "portraying a sad person in an acting class."

Laughter and Tears

Laughter, another release of emotional stress, was the subject of recent research conducted by a Stanford University professor of psychiatry. His name, coincidentally, is William F. Fry, Jr. He says laughter stimulates the brain's production of catecholamines and really *is* the best medicine. Fry refers to laughing as "stationary jogging," since the heart rate may double during a long, hard laughing jag. When a person stops laughing, muscles relax and the heart rate drops below normal as if the body had just finished strenuous exercise. Laughter also helps relieve fear and dispel anger, Fry says.[6] Norman Cousins' claim that laughter helped cure his usually fatal collagen disease received world-wide attention several years ago, when he replaced prescribed pain killers with viewing the TV show "Candid Camera" and Marx brothers films, and reading humorous books. "I made the joyous discovery that ten minutes of genuine belly laughter had an anesthetic effect and would give me at least two hours of pain-free sleep," he wrote in *Anatomy of an Illness as Perceived by the Patient.*[7]

While laughing and crying are often considered opposites, they can be closely related and, in some cases, are difficult to distinguish from each other. One subject wrote, "Some people don't know whether I'm laughing or crying." And fifty-eight subjects in our study reported laughing until they cried, with the teary laughing episodes lasting from a few seconds to thirty minutes. One subject reported shedding tears more often and longer when laughing than when crying for other reasons. The majority of these episodes occurred with family, friends, or coworkers while "cracking jokes" or "amused by friend's story." Reminiscing while "looking at old family photos" made a few subjects laugh with tears, and one subject reported shedding tears of laughter while "talking about the craziness of data analysis and using computers." Hilarious incidents caused some subjects to both weep and laugh. One such episode involved a man who accidentally ran over a tomato plant with a rototiller, which sent tomatoes flying in every direction. The humor of that chaotic situation not only brought tears to his wife's eyes when it happened but also later as she related the story to friends. About one-fourth of the tears of laughter were shed while watching TV—again, "M*A*S*H" was mentioned most often—or live comedy routines.

I was amazed at the great variety of situations our subjects reported as having stimulated their tears. According to our crying behavior study and the correspondence I received about emotional crying, adult tears can appear in response to almost any imaginable emotional situation. Regardless of what stimulates your emotional tears, you can be fairly certain that others also cry in similar circumstances.

10

Who Says Big Boys Don't Cry?

I like a man who can cry.

Jessamyn West

From early childhood men and boys are taught to hide certain feelings. "Don't cry; act like a man," they are told when they feel pain or sadness. This negative attitude toward male feelings and tears was apparent even twenty-two centuries ago, when the Greek Stoic philosopher Epictetus wrote: "If Odysseus wept, he was no good man." Boabdil, the last Moorish king to rule Granada, was run out of northern Spain by Christian armies in 1492. Before he rode off to his final battle, his own mother reportedly had said, "You cry like a woman because you do not know how to defend yourself like a man." Some proverbs handed down in various cultures advise one to be leery of men who weep. This one from Yugoslavia warns: "Trust not a weeping man, still less a woman who speaks of her chastity." Another maxim from India offers similar advice: "A laughing woman and a crying man should never be trusted."

Men have been expected to be tough, dominant, decisive, logical, and certainly always in control, since it was their duty to protect women and children and run the world. This stoicism inflicted on men left little room for expressing emotions, especially those which involve tears. Anger was one of the few emotional reactions that was considered appropriate for "real men."

While mythology and early classics abound with female weeping, there are few instances of male tears. Renaissance writers, however, refer to them unabashedly. Shakespeare's male characters often speak of their tears, and sixteenth century English poet Edward Young wrote, "Scorn the proud man that is ashamed to weep." Two centuries later American philosopher George Santayana said, "The young man who has not wept is a savage; the old man who will not laugh is a fool."

When Men May Cry

Modern society seems to feel that sometimes it is OK for men to cry, and sometimes it is not. Little boys are still often admonished not to cry, and most men have a long way to go before they become comfortable with their own and other men's tears. American society generally accepts men who shed tears related to successes and failures in the sports arena and often cries along with its heroes. Fans sympathized with New York Giants football star Y.A. Tittle when he cried after losing the game that gave the season championship to the Chicago Bears. No one thought less of Mickey Mantle as he sobbed in the New York Yankee locker room after injuries benched him during a World Series game. When Babe Ruth wept openly before 60,000 fans, who packed Yankee Stadium to pay tribute to their cancer-stricken hero, the fans cried along with him. And there was not a dry eye in the stadium as Lou Gehrig said, "I'm proud to be a Yankee" in his 1939 farewell speech.

Flowing tears and in some cases uncontrollable sobbing were not uncommon in male gold medal winners at the 1984 Olympic Summer Games in Los Angeles. Koji Gushiken of Japan began shedding tears almost the moment he learned he had cinched the gold medal in the men's all-around gymnastics competition. Gushiken was elated and overwhelmed with his scores—none lower than 9.90—in what would probably be his last Olympic performance. Often described as "the little man with the big heart," the twenty-seven-year-old bank teller wept openly, often sobbing into a white towel, for about fifteen minutes while the other gymnasts finished their routines. His tears flowed again when Japan's national anthem played during the award ceremony.

Later that same August evening, Jeff Blatnick, who had won a battle with cancer only two years earlier, captured a gold medal for the United States in Greco-Roman wrestling. During an interview immediately after winning the medal, the 220-pound wrestler, who had lost his spleen to Hodgkin's disease in 1982, could not hold back his tears as he thanked his high school, his family, and his coach for their unfaltering support. Blatnick began sobbing as the commentator, who was also choked up, congratulated him:

"I'm a happy dude," said Blatnick through his tears.

"The crowd's happy with you too, Jeff."

"I'm sorry . . . I can't talk," said Blatnick, whose tears and intense emotion seemed to endear the audience and viewers to the herculean American who had overcome tremendous adversity to win the first U.S. medal in Greco-Roman wrestling.

Americans also appear to condone on-stage and off-stage male tears in the entertainment field. Conductor Leonard Bernstein broke down and cried when the audience at the Kennedy Center in Washington D.C. reacted with thunderous applause to the first performance of his *Mass*; after learning that the Muscular Dystrophy Telethon had received 9.2 million dollars in pledges, Jerry Lewis wept copiously while he sang "You'll Never Walk Alone"; and Alan King could not hold back his tears that erupted at the opening of a medical center in Jerusalem bearing his name. "Tonight Show" viewers who watched Jimmy Stewart read a poem he had written shortly after the death of his beloved golden retriever, Beau, will long remember his cracking voice and genuine tears as he read the final verse about how much he missed his untrained, exuberant, lovable friend.

Tears shed by some political figures were not received harshly either, and, in some cases, the ability to shed tears was considered a positive quality. Abraham Lincoln was proud of the fact he could weep in sympathy and for his own relief. John L. Lewis wept when he took his mine workers out of the CIO. In 1968, shortly after Senator Eugene McCarthy dropped out of the presidential race, he attended a rally in Los Angeles. He broke into tears as he was greeted by thousands of students chanting "Write in McCarthy . . . Write in McCarthy . . . Write in McCarthy." Six-foot-three Lyndon Johnson cried intensely when he stood beside Gandhi's grave in India. And, finally, during 1978, the year in which he lost his battle with cancer, Hubert Humphrey wept in public several times. At one point he made this often quoted remark: "A man without tears is a man without a heart."

When Men May Not

Sometimes men's tears shed in public are not acceptable. The American public was not receptive to Edmund Muskie's tears, shed during the 1972 presidential campaign. When expressing his disappointment with a newspaper publisher who had run a letter implying unkind things about Muskie's wife, the Senator from Maine openly shed tears on national TV. Some political observers feel his on-camera weeping all but ended his chance to be a serious contender, perhaps because the public considered his tearful expression of emotion as an indication that he had not yet developed the toughness politicians need to withstand the public smears and criticism against not only oneself but one's family as well. Although Muskie's tears turned voters off, the public apparently still considers certain phenomena moving enough to make even "strong men" weep.

Even though male athletes, entertainers, and political leaders may weep publicly, many men still consider expressing emotion themselves other than anger or exuberance (such as after winning a game) as unmasculine and a sign of weakness. Writer Robert Farrar Capon, who spent thirty years as a parish priest, reported that the saddest part of his job was to minister to terminally ill men who could not express sadness or disappointment. Their inveterate dread of being "little boys" condemned them to go right on "pretending they were tough even when they soon would no longer be any kind of boy at all."

The feminist movement, which gained momentum following the publication of Betty Friedan's *The Feminine*

Mystique in 1964, encouraged increased male sensitivity and made it easier for some men to be more expressive of love, tenderness, and vulnerability. But tears can be misleading. While they are often considered a sign of sensitivity in men, this is not always the case. The inability to express emotion by crying does not necessarily indicate an inability to feel emotion, just as the ability to cry does not guarantee sensitivity. One European recently told me of Nazi soldiers who had killed children with flame throwers during World War II and then cried two days later as they sang "Silent Night."

Crying and Masculinity

In 1972 former NFL star Rosie Grier did his part to encourage boys and men to openly show emotion, and to cry when he sang "It's All Right to Cry" on the hit record album "Free to Be You and Me." At the end of the song he says, "It's all right to cry, little boy. I know some big boys who cry, too."

While it is slightly more permissible for men to express their warm, hurt, gentle, or fearful feelings in certain situations, many men still vent their pain, guilt, anger, and frustration in a macho manner by swearing, getting inebriated, mistreating others, working or jogging "it" off. Males who feel that expressing emotions with or without tears is unacceptable sometimes cover up their strong feelings only to release them later in an inappropriate way.

Several studies conducted in the last few years offer some speculations about male tears. In a 1978 study based on telephone interviews with 680 married couples, social psychologists Catherine E. Ross and John Mirowsky reported that men who adhere to traditional masculine roles are likely to cry less than nontraditional men when they are sad. Ross and Mirowsky surmised that although men with greater socioeconomic status may have less reason for sadness, they are more likely to cry when feeling sad because men with higher incomes and education levels also tend to be less traditional.[1]

In 1982 D. G. Williams studied seventy male and seventy female British adults and found that males and females who identify more strongly with the feminine sex-role stereotype cry more than those who identify more strongly with the male sex-role stereotype.[2]

Thomas Bradbury, a Wake Forest University sociologist, attempted to verify Williams' findings in a survey of 182 male and 119 female college students, but his study did not confirm Williams' results. Bradbury found that increased identification with the feminine sex role is correlated with increased crying in men and women, but women with a higher masculine score cry *more*, not less.[3]

Another sociologist, Clinton Jesser, surveyed eighty-six male and eighty-six female college students about their experiences with and reactions to crying. He determined that males are less supportive than females when others cry, especially when other men cry. In spite of their apparent unwillingness to support and become involved with others on a deep emotional level, many of the male subjects expressed a desire to cry more and to feel more positive about their own crying. Jesser surmised from his and other studies that "men do not tend to define their well-being as requiring personal socio-emotional exchange and the disclosure and processing of feelings as much as do women, but that for many men who do enter this processs of [becoming emotionally intimate] . . . , they find enough difficulty, confusion, and even negative reinforcement to pull back from it and 'tough it out.'" He attributes this unwillingness to engage in constructive emotional processing to these men's own inner demands, expectations, and images of themselves. This overall view of self-sufficiency and self-control that men often have of themselves could contribute to the negative way they interpret others' reactions when they do express tender emotion, Jesser concluded.[4]

Although hormonal differences may contribute to the dissimilarities between male and female crying behavior, social conditioning also plays a very important role in determining whether or not males cry. Anti-crying socialization begins in childhood when males are told that "big boys don't cry" or when they are ridiculed by their peers when they do. They are taught that tears are a sign of weakness. In an attempt to eliminate the humiliation they feel when they cry, boys try to not show certain emotions to others. What often happens is that they hide their feelings so well from others that they eventually hide them even from themselves. Unlike men, women have not been forced into a role of always being strong and in control. Their ability to cry freely is a sign of liberation. I think no one should always have to be the Rock of Gibralter; everyone should be allowed moments of vulnerability and be able to disclose feelings to others.

Men Who Want to Cry

I have received several letters from men ranging in age from the twenties to the mid-forties who have not cried since childhood and want to recover their lost ability to cry. Their crying histories and requests are similar to this New York man, who wrote:

> I am a forty-four-year-old gentleman who has not been able to cry since the age of eleven. There have been several incidents in my life which should have brought tears. I yearn to find the relief of tears again before I die. Any suggestion from you would be highly regarded.

In response to men who want to regain their ability to cry, I assure them that their lack of tears is not unusual in our modern society. I then encourage them to begin by trying to reclaim their emotions and get in touch with their own feelings. Sometimes a psychologist or counselor who understands the need to own and express feelings can help them change their pattern of dealing with emotional stress.

Like the men who write me about their inability to cry and many other young men, I stopped crying at about twelve years of age and do not remember crying at all during the next twelve years. I do not know why I stopped and do not recall making a conscious effort to stop—I just stopped. During my teenage years I experienced many highly emotional events, and yet I never cried. As I mentioned in Chapter One, when I was a twenty-four-year-old graduate student, I became concerned about not having cried for so many years. I wondered if it was normal, and even if it was normal or average for men. I wondered if this was the kind of person I wanted to be. I decided it was not. I wanted to experience and express my feelings more, to be in touch with life and myself. So I consciously made an effort to get back in touch with my feelings, to allow myself to get upset when events warranted it, to give myself permission to feel sadness and pain, and to *cry*. It took a long time to accomplish that, but the result was worth the effort. I do cry occasionally with flowing tears when I'm very upset, and my eyes fill with tears on many occasions when I am touched by something.

Because I have been willing to expose my feelings to others, I know myself better now, which is one of the potential benefits of self-disclosure and crying. If you hide your true self and feelings from others so they will like you or approve of you, then the person they like and approve of is not really you. When we teach children to suppress their feelings and not to cry, we do them a great disservice by robbing them of one of nature's adaptive responses to emotional stress.

11

To Cry or Not to Cry

Sorrows which find no vent in tears may soon make other organs weep.

Sir Henry Maudsley

Hans Selye spent most of his life studying the effects of stress on our bodies and how our systems struggle to adapt to our ever-changing environment. He emphasizes that all stress is not harmful and distinguishes between *eustress*—positive stimulation and challenge that help us achieve—and *distress* —harmful, unpleasant stress, often the result of too many or too abrupt changes, boredom, frustration, or lack of purpose.[1]

Since individuals react differently to the same stimuli, we must take heed from the Seven Sages who advised, "Know thyself." One person's distress may be someone else's eustress. In his books Selye writes that we must not avoid stress but instead use it creatively to motivate personal achievement and at the same time maintain a sense of inner balance.

Stress and Disease

Until the last few decades, only Selye and a handful of researchers devoted their lives to studying stress and its relationship to disease. Stress and its ill-effects have always been a part of living, but not until recently has the subject become the focus of much scientific research—perhaps because the world seems to be suffering from a "stress epidemic." In a list of the 200 top-selling drugs in the United States in 1984, Inderal (a drug prescribed for high blood pressure) was number one; Valium (a tranquilizer) was number four; Tagamet (an ulcer medication) was number seven.[2] In response to this stress epidemic, medicine has branched off into new areas in psychobiology which focus on ways to combat stress-related illness and psychoneuroimmunology, a field that explores how emotional states affect the body's defense systems.

No one knows whether life is really more stressful now or if we are just more aware of the world's uncertainties—nuclear threat, unemployment, abusive crimes—brought into our homes everyday on TV. I think people tend to imagine they live in a more stressful world than people in other time periods. Those early American pioneers who cleared the land, and faced harsh winters after poor harvests probably experienced as much stress as any modern suburbanite. And they had little medicine to treat illness in those days. People died of polio, smallpox, malaria, bacterial pneumonia, anthrax, and other diseases that are either prevented or easily treated today.

The subjects in our adult crying behavior study were asked, "Were you under any unusual emotional stress during the last month? Please describe." Over 40% of the male and female subjects responded that they *were* under unusual stress during the month they recorded their crying episodes. We thought this was strange, so we separated the responses of those who indicated unusual stress into two categories: major, when death, divorce, or major illness was involved; and minor, for other reasons such as concern over a college examination. Of the 43% who reported they were under unusual emotional stress, we found that only 16% attributed their stress to major events, while 84% who responded "yes" to the stress question gave relatively minor reasons for their stress. Evidently, it is not unusual for people to feel they are under "unusual" emotional stress, even when no major life situation is threatened. In view of how we identify stress, it is not surprising that one of today's fastest growing fields is stress-management, a multi-million dollar-a-year business. Classes in biofeedback, transcendental meditation, yoga, autogenic training, muscle-relaxation, or other methods of stress-reduction are being taught at hospitals, medical centers, and many major corporations.

Humans release stress in a variety of ways such as fighting, yelling, laughing, talking rapidly, exercising, and crying. In his book *The Vital Balance,* Dr. Karl Menninger writes, "Weeping is perhaps the most human and most universal of all relief measures."[3] While emotional tears are only one of many release mechanisms for an overload of strong emotion and stress, they are easier to measure than other stress releasers. Although asking persons how they feel about various aspects of crying is subjective, the actual tears need no interpretation. They are either present or absent. Tears are one of the few aspects of involuntary emotional expression that provide something concrete to measure. Thus, the role which the release of tears plays in stress management lends itself to experimental verification.

Often when researchers want to learn about the purpose of a physiological process, they study those who do not have the ability to carry out the process. If emotional crying does make people feel better, as many suggest, then what happens to persons who cannot shed tears under stress?

In 1949 C. M. Riley described a group of children with two common features: They were unable to shed tears, and they had an abnormal reaction to mild anxiety. In these children emotional stress produced a number of symptoms described by Riley which included "transient extreme elevation of blood pressure, excessive sweating, salivation to the point of drooling, and the development of sharply demarcated erythematous blotches on the skin. . . ." While more is now known about this syndrome, called familial dysautonomia, it is still not clear whether the inability of these children to secrete tears with their crying contributes to their extremely abnormal physical reactions to stress.[4] Science has known for years that excessive emotional stress causes the release of hormones and other substances into the blood altering our chemical balance. It is known that the pituitary gland releases beta-endorphin, an opiate-like compound, and the hormones ACTH and prolactin into the blood stream in response to stress. As discussed earlier, stress also releases the catecholamines—epinephrine (adrenaline) from the adrenal gland, and norepinephrine from the sympathetic nervous system. Several scientists, including psychiatrist Daniel Funkenstein, have gone a step further and suggested that the particular emotion involved may determine which catecholamine is discharged into the blood.[5]

It is thought by many that there is a relationship between the suppression of emotions, psychological health, and disease. It is also generally accepted that crying is one way of expressing and releasing emotion. "Tears are the safety valves of the heart when too much pressure is laid upon it," wrote Albert Richard Smith. If emotional tearing reduces the effects of stress, then we may increase our susceptibility to a variety of physical and psychological problems when we suppress our tears. Selye writes, "We are just beginning to see that many common diseases are largely due to errors in our adaptive response to stress. . . . Many nervous and emotional disturbances, high blood pressure, gastric and duodenal ulcers, certain types of sexual, allergic, cardiovascular, and renal derangements appear to be essentially *diseases of adaptation.*"[6]

Crying Frequency and Disease

As yet, no one has done any research measuring crying frequency in relation to illness. However, a study to examine the relationship between suppressed tears and specific stress-related disorders and between the free expression of tears and health was conducted at the University of Pittsburgh School of Nursing in 1979 by Margaret Crepeau. She recognized that tears are one factor in emotional expression which can be explored in health and illness.

One hundred thirty-seven male and female subjects from Pittsburgh and other areas of the United States who were either healthy or had an ulcer or colitis, participated in the research. They filled out a three-part questionnaire to determine (1) how likely a person is to cry in a variety of situations, (2) what the person generally feels about crying, (3) what tears personally meant to the person. Crepeau found that healthy persons (both male and female) are more likely to cry and have a more positive attitude toward tears than those persons with ulcers and colitis, two conditions thought to be aggravated by stress.[7] So it is possible that anti-crying socialization may have adverse consequences on health.

While Crepeau's research is one of the few studies specifically exploring the relationship between tear suppression and disease, other theories concerning the role of tears in disease have been presented. A three-year study at the State University of New York Downstate Medical Center suggested that depression often precedes the onset of the common cold. Based on this information, Merl Jackel speculated that colds may be "symbolically repressed tears."[8] (This speculation seems to ignore the role of viruses in causing colds.) Other speculative theories linking asthma, urticaria (hives), and other physical conditions with the suppression of tears have also appeared in the scientific literature.[9, 10, 11, 12]

Tears Alleviate Grief

Folk wisdom and literature contain many references to the fact that humans and animals become ill and die from grief. Until recently this epitaph could be found engraved on tombstones: "Died of a broken heart." During the last century scientific studies on bereavement have confirmed that the loss of a loved one, particularly a spouse, can lead to ill health and even death. Researchers found that widows with acquaintances who made it easy for them to cry and express their intense feelings were healthier than widows who experienced less encouragement from others to weep and discuss their feelings of grief.[13] This information supports the speakers in Alfred Lord Tennyson's famous passage in his poem "The Princess" written in 1847.

Home they brought her warrior dead.
She nor swooned nor uttered cry;
All her maidens, watching, said,
"She must weep or she will die."

Rees and Lutkins (1967) found that widowers are more likely to die soon after the death of their spouse than widows, and the overall risk for bereaved male relatives is twice that of females.[14] In a similar extensive 1981 study, Knut Helsing and his associates found mortality rates were about the same for widowed as for married women, but were considerably higher for widowed men than married men.[15] Dr. George Engels' research on sudden deaths found that more men than women die following a distressing major life event, and men died at an earlier age.[16] Dr. W. Dewi Rees offers an explanation for this higher incidence of male deaths following a death in the family in his article, "Bereavement and Illness," in the *Journal of Thanatology.* He writes, "It is conceivable that the increased mortality associated with bereavement found among men, when compared with women, may be due to the greater repression of overt feeling traditionally required of men and to the cultural taboo that prevents a proper healthy expression of their grief."[17]

The importance of crying is emphasized in literature written to help people resolve their grief. In their book *About Mourning: Support and Guidance for the Bereaved,* Savine Weizman and Phyllis Kamm explain that mourning is a gradual, natural process with many phases: shock, abandonment, denial, disbelief, withdrawal, guilt, resentment, anger, hostility, sadness, despair, self-pity, and integration. Eventual healing and recovery will take place if the process of mourning is completed. "Important components of the [mourning] process are crying, talking, sharing, and having permission from yourself and others to engage in these releases," they write. Weizman and Kamm emphasize the necessity of sharing feelings, words, and tears with a relative, friend, clergyman, therapist, support group, or someone who has had a similar experience.[18]

In their pamphlet "When Your Mate Dies" Weizman and Kamm write:

You may feel very alone, abandoned and as if no one understands. You may feel constantly on the verge of tears. One young widow related, "I cried every day for a year."

Most important of all, don't be afraid to cry, don't be afraid to feel your pain and express your grief. Until you feel the full gamut of your hurt, anger, hostility, and sadness, you will not be able to move forward to acceptance and live a full life. . . . But happiness and sadness can coexist and you will find there is still more to life than tears.[19]

Crying appears to be an essential part of the overall grieving process, which may take years to complete.

Learning to Release Tears

Some subjects in our adult crying behavior study expressed concern over the fact that while they could cry for a variety of what they considered unimportant reasons, they did not shed tears over major events such as death and serious illness. One subject wanted to know "why I cry over impersonal things and don't cry over personal things." Another subject wrote that she "found it interesting that when crying is appropriate, such as my grandfather's funeral or serious illness, I don't cry. Makes me wonder if I'm cold, but I do cry easily for sentimental reasons or thoughts, or if someone close to me cries or when watching TV." She surmised, "I must need this to release pent-up emotions."

Several persons in the behavior study expressed concern that they seemed to have lost their ability to cry. One subject wrote, "I'd give anything if I still could cry. It helped me feel I could go on and overcome the problem." Another wrote, "Wish I could cry, but it has been ingrained in my mind that crying is not an answer to anything; so I am no longer able to cry over nonmajor events." Some women who feel that they need a good cry to relieve stress but can't get the tears started, seek out sad movies. For years, *Wuthering Heights* was one of the classic tearjerkers. *Terms of Endearment* heads the list of recent movies that elicit tears, according to a preliminary survey we conducted for a study to determine which movies make men and women cry.

Being able to produce tears at will is a skill many actors and actresses develop as part of their theatrical training. While some actors use menthol crystals (or some type of eye irritant) to stimulate tears, and others substitute drops of glycerin for tear drops (especially in movie retakes), many actors prefer to trigger their theatrical tears with real emotion.

Kate Fuglei, an actress from the Tyrone Guthrie Theater in Minneapolis, described in a phone interview how she brought forth her theatrical tears:

> Ideally, I would like to always be able to cry real tears during a performance. Sometimes the tears come easily. On nights when I'm really into it, really connected with the character, the tears just come. Recently, I played a fourteen-year-old who was about to have an abortion. Most nights I felt I was the character and could believe that I was in the situation, so during the sad, wrenching scenes I cried real tears.
>
> Other times I'm just not into it. Things have been rushed before the performance, the car wouldn't start, or I don't feel well, or something personal is bothering me. I'm not living the character. During times such as these I use emotional recall to generate tears. Usually two instances in my childhood or one incident I experienced as an adult help me cry. I think of specific details—how someone's face looked, something in the room, anything that brings back strong emotion that went along with the episodes.[20]

Actors and actresses learn to use such emotional memory— a technique developed by Constantin Stanislavski—to elicit tears as part of their theatrical training. Each one must search for unhappy events in their lives that will trigger tears.

Although just thinking of sad events may bring tears occasionally, it fails to consistently release tears.

In her book, *Respect for Acting,* Uta Hagen gives precise instructions for the technique described by the Guthrie actress to induce weeping on stage. She advises actors to find their own "release object" connected in some way to the sad event they are focusing on. These seemingly insignificant objects—a ring on a finger, a painting on the wall, the smell of freshly brewed tea, the sound of raindrops hitting a tin roof— are more effective at triggering tears than dwelling on the essence of the painful event. Hagen herself used this technique for years without understanding why it worked. She later learned that the release objects may have been unconsciously perceived and thus bypass the conscious voice that tells us "Don't lose control."[21] Regardless of the reasons, this technique is used successfully by many actors.

To teach their clients to release tears, some grief counselors recommend deliberately recalling a memory by going to a specific place or finding something that belonged to the person that died. Certain music or artwork done by the deceased works in some cases. If their clients feel choked up with tears but cannot let themselves cry, some counselors suggest they pant rapidly. Supposedly, the abrupt breaths help make crying possible for some persons.[22, 23]

For those who cannot learn to cry by drawing on their emotional memory, a few simple suggestions for releasing tears offered by a Los Angeles psychologist may help. Anthony Tinn suggests that persons may be able to reclaim their ability to cry by (1) actively challenging the old cliches about why one should not cry, (2) expressing feelings associated with the need to cry, and (3) being with someone who is comfortable with crying when crying is appropriate.[24]

Ingeborg Day interviewed a cross-section of the population for the article "What Makes You Cry?" in *Ms* magazine. One woman's mother passed on her method of dealing with life's blows: Peel and mince onions to start the tears and don't stop until you feel better.[25] Perhaps her irritant tears help start her emotional tears flowing.

I feel that many persons lose the ability to cry emotional tears because of social conditioning. When children (particularly boys) are told crying is childish, or when others react negatively to our tears as we grow older, we try to hold back our tears. However, it is difficult to feel very sad or hurt without crying, and we soon learn that it is easier not to cry if we do not allow ourselves to feel strongly in the first place. If we suppress the emotions that cause our tears, we avoid the feelings of embarrassment or loss of control or vulnerability that can accompany a weeping outburst. As I mentioned earlier, individuals who learn to hide their emotions from others may eventually hide them so well that they no longer know what or how they feel. (Obviously, there are some who seem to do well without crying and do not want to change.) For others, perhaps the only way to reverse the problem and regain the ability to express emotions is to work with a psychologist or other health professional who will help them to experience, own, and express their feelings. When we reclaim emotional expression, begin to know ourselves better, and thus become more fully human, we may also be able to once again utilize one of the few physiological functions that separates humans from other animals—emotional weeping.

Uncontrollable Tears

While some are unable to cry even when they try, others have the opposite problem of not being able to control their crying. Just as the lack of tears makes many persons feel deprived of the relief of weeping, those with an abundance of uncontrollable tears often feel deprived in other ways. Many people who cry readily often consider their inability to stop the flow of tears as a social handicap, especially in their communication with others. "I cry often from a few seconds to thirty seconds," wrote one subject. "I'm very sensitive about these episodes and try to hide my tears. It's a social handicap which creates much strain for me at weddings, funerals, concerts, recitals, movies, ceremonies, etc." Other subjects reported that crying interfered with their ability to communicate their feelings to others. "I cry easily. Some things I want to say very badly I can't get out at all." Another appeared only to have trouble relaying her positive feelings.

I find it difficult to tell others when I have strong, good feelings toward them or want to tell them how great I think they are or tell them I think what they did or said was wonderful, warm, beautiful, or whatever. Very often I give the opposite impression of what I'm feeling because I'm trying so hard to keep from crying and instead of conveying the warmness I'm feeling, I appear strained and unpleasantly tense, when actually I'm feeling very positive and loving toward the person or situation. HELP!!

I have received several letters from women troubled by excessive crying. In some cases excessive crying may indicate a physical or psychological problem in which case the individual should seek professional help. But according to our study the range of crying frequency in normal, apparently healthy individuals varies from zero to seven episodes per month for men and zero to twenty-nine episodes per month for women.

If individuals cry in excess of this range, it is unusual but does not necessarily indicate a problem. If the crying is so excessive as to be problematic to them or interfere with their functioning, they should seek professional help to find out if physical or mental illness has affected their crying. We are currently studying individuals troubled with excessive crying and a very low threshold for crying to determine if they may have altered levels of hormones, which contribute to their problem.

Obviously there are times when it is best and in your own self-interest to hold back your tears, just as it is advisable to sometimes control your temper. And there are times when you feel the need to be "strong" for someone else. Many how-to-attain-success articles written for working women allude to the importance of controlling emotions in the workplace to reinforce the impression of stability, strength, and competence. Of course, there are times when it is not good to be in tears, for example, when a nurse or physician treats an injured child. However, I have seen women cry at work when their crying very effectively made their boss feel like a real heel and insensitive jerk. Seriously, crying at work is probably something that only rarely should be prevented. Although many people seem to feel tears do not belong on the job, we need to learn to accept crying and human emotion in the workplace.

Perhaps someday we will discover why some people shed tears so often and so readily. Until then these persons with a tendency toward lacrimosity will have to find a way to deal with their untamed tears. This account, written by a woman who has learned to accept her tears and is teaching others to accept them, may help other very frequent criers who often fight a losing battle to control their tears:

> I often shed tears when I feel angry, hurt, sympathetic, or disappointed with myself or others. I may cry when someone pays me a meaningful compliment about my work or my family.
>
> Until about four years ago, my uncontrollable tears were responsible for many embarrassing, frustrating, and annoying situations. Tears interfered with communication as I tried to settle conflicts and relate strong feelings—both good and bad. Instead of holding my ground, I would retreat and hold back what I wanted to say because I knew my crying would be misunderstood or cause others to overreact.
>
> It was often much easier and less traumatic to stifle my desire to be assertive, show warm feelings, or just carry on a normal conversation by withdrawing rather than risk exposing the tears about to erupt. When discussions were cut short because I felt as if I may cry, the encounters ended up unsatisfying and unproductive, not only for me but also for the others involved. Occasionally I managed to check the tears, but usually they ran down my face and neck before I could react. Stopping the tears took tremendous energy and concentration and left me exhausted and drained, giving others the impression that something was drastically wrong.

It dawned on me one day that, even though I couldn't always control my tears, I perhaps could learn to keep talking and not withdraw whenever I felt the tears coming. If I couldn't lick them, maybe I could learn to join them. I promised myself I would try to keep on talking or carry on whatever I was doing in spite of the tears, explain that I cried easily and my tears didn't mean anything serious and ask others to not let my tears interfere with our conversation or activity.

Shortly after I decided to go public with my tears, I began a new job. During the first few months the owner and I spent one hour a week reviewing my work and planning short-term and long-term objectives. During one of our meetings following a hectic week both at home and at work, he pointed out several major errors and poor decisions I had made. As we came to the fourth error, tears flooded my eyes and splashed onto the paper before I could catch them. I resisted the strong urge to excuse myself, head for the rest room to collect my wits and reapply make-up, then return and apologize for the interruption. I stayed put and said, "I cry very easily, but I'm not crying because of the criticism. It's more from the frustration with lack of time and because I was careless and didn't catch the mistakes. Please (sniff, sniff) ignore these tears. I want to hear what you have to say about my work."

Much to my surprise he said he had planned to ignore my crying before I said anything. His office manager who had been with him for many years often cried easily, and he had learned if he just went ahead with the discussion, everything was fine.

It was not nearly that easy to tell some persons to try to disregard my tears. Many became very uneasy when I cried and although I could carry on through the tears, I found that some people couldn't. Few persons are totally at ease with my tears but after the second or third crying session, they seem to be more tolerant and less uneasy.

The following explanation seems to satisfy all but the most dubious persons. "I cry very easily over many things. Please understand that just because I am crying does not necessarily mean I'm very upset and that I want us to stop talking. I know it's hard to overlook these dumb drops sloshing all over my face, but please, for my sake, try to ignore them. I'm trying hard to not let these tears interrupt and stop conversations. I'd appreciate it very much if we can just carry on where we left off."

The main thing I've learned is that if I am comfortable with my tears others will be too. Even though I still wish I could control my crying, I feel that by learning to accept my frequent tears I am less handicapped by them.

Many persons with whom I come in contact often understand the fountains that readily spring from my eyes with most strong emotion and react to them about the same way as they would to other body language or reactions—drumming fingers on the table, a change in voice pitch, a nervous twitch, fidgeting with hair, or clearing one's throat. They realize my tears are like unpredictable geysers that I'm trying to deal with. They know the tears are not there to manipulate or because I'm very upset or overwrought, but are just a quirk of mine.

When I speak to various groups about crying, I always emphasize that I do not necessarily recommend that people *try* to cry, but rather that they allow themselves to cry when they feel like crying. I think many people need to learn that it is OK to cry and that they do not have to be strong all the time. One man told his therapist that he was afraid to let go and cry because he was afraid he would never stop. He and many others need to learn that they will not have a nervous breakdown if they just totally let go and cry and sob; they can give themselves permission to feel and express their feelings as long as they do not hurt others. We all have the right to be human, to feel, to cry. There is no need to deprive ourselves of the natural healthy release of emotional tears.

The next time you feel tears coming and struggle to hold them back, think of Mr. Bumbles' lines from Charles Dickens' *Oliver Twist*: "It opens the lungs, washes the countenance, exercises the eyes, and softens down the temper. So cry away!"

12

How Adults View Their Own Tears

Weeping makes the heart grow lighter.
Yiddish Proverb

The notion that emotional crying eases tension and helps humans feel better is certainly nothing new. Throughout history the catharsis of weeping has been expressed frequently in poetry and literature. Over twenty centuries ago the Roman poet Ovid wrote, "It is a relief to weep. Grief is satisfied and carried off by tears." A few years later, Seneca, a Roman philosopher and Nero's adviser, succinctly observed, "Weeping lightens woe."

Proverbs about the benefit of psychogenic tears have been handed down from generation to generation.

Learn weeping, and thou shall gain laughing.
(German)
Tears soothe suffering eyes. *(Persian)*
There is laughter that follows every weeping.
(Persian)
What soap is for the body, tears are for the soul.
(Jewish)

While humans intuitively have known for centuries that crying makes us feel better, our behavior study was the first to scientifically confirm that people feel better after crying.

This chapter is based primarily on the normal subjects' responses to questions that accompanied the diary.

How many times a month, on an average, do you shed tears because of emotional stress?

Men estimated shedding tears once a month compared to the women's estimate of four times per month. The actual crying frequency (5.3 for women, 1.4 for men) reported in the diaries by the subjects was very close to their estimates of how many times a month they usually cried.

Do you generally feel better, worse, or no different after you have cried?

Most of the subjects reported feeling better after crying. Eighty-five percent of females and 73% of males indicated they feel better after shedding tears compared to only 5% of the females and 4% of the males who reported feeling worse after crying. Ten percent of the females and 15% of the males reported no difference in their emotional state before and after crying.

Many subjects agreed with the subject who wrote, "Crying is a release mechanism for built-up emotions." Others indicated crying brings relief from tension and helps them feel better, and some mentioned the cleansing quality of tears:

"Tears seem to wash out the bad feelings."

"It's a kind of cleansing, finally letting go."

A few subjects thought crying helped them get rid of oppressive feelings that wear them down, or as one subject wrote, "I feel the heaviness has been lifted." Several subjects compared the release of tears to "an escape valve" that "gets rid of the down feeling" to release "something I've kept inside." Others seemed to agree with Alfred Austin's observation about the rejuvenating quality of tears: "Tears are summer showers to the soul," when they reported feeling "refreshed after a good cry" and "more relaxed, content, calm."

One woman who called to discuss the crying study brought my attention to this Spanish proverb: "Tears wash the cobwebs from your attic." Some subjects indicated, as she did, that crying helped them regain cognizance of their situation and strength to carry on. One subject described her post-crying feelings as "clearer, easier to see reality." One subject wrote that, after a good cry, she was "more willing to deal with the situation." Another responded that crying "helps me feel as if I can go on and overcome the problem." A few subjects responded that they felt better after crying because the tears "helped them share feelings and talk things out."

A few subjects who rarely or never cry indicated they wished they were able to feel relief from tears, but they just could not cry even when they tried. A few subjects reported that they felt worse if they felt like crying but, for some reason, suppressed their tears.

It is not clear how humans manage to alleviate emotional stress when they do not cry and what adverse effects they may experience from suppressing their tears. Shakespeare's Richard in *King Henry VI* lamented the consequences of his inability to express his strong emotion in tears or words:

> I cannot weep; for all my body's moisture
> Scarce serves to quench my furnace-burning heart:
> Nor can my tongue unload my heart's great burden;
> For the self-same wind that I should speak withal
> Is kindling coals, that fire all my breast,
> And burn me with flames, that tears would quench.
> To weep is to make less the depth of grief:
> Tears, then, for babes; blows and revenge for me!

About one fourth of the subjects who reported feeling better after crying added some stipulations. Some felt worse when others saw them cry and better only when they cried alone. Others only felt better when someone was present when they cried, so they had someone to talk to.

For some subjects, the reason for the tears determined whether they felt better or worse after crying. Some reported feeling better only if their tears came from self-pity, frustration, or anger, while others felt worse if crying for any or all of those three reasons. While a few reported feeling better if crying for "personal reasons" and no different if they cried over movies or books, others felt the opposite was true for them.

Nine subjects who reported feeling "less tense" and "mentally relieved" after crying added that they suffered physically when they shed tears. Of the few subjects who indicated they felt worse after crying, several gave "physical discomfort" as the reason. The unpleasant symptoms that accompanied crying included headaches, swollen eyes and face, and a drained, tired, weak feeling. This perhaps explains why some reported feeling better after a short cry, but worse following longer crying sessions.

I have received many letters from persons who suffer similar adverse physical reactions to emotional crying. Several persons wrote saying they noticed that tears shed for different reasons—grief, joy, rapture, frustration—seemed to be noticeably different, with some having a more stinging sensation and tasting saltier than others. No one knows why some people have adverse physical reactions to crying while others do not. Some subjects felt they were allergic to a substance excreted in their tears. However, this has never been confirmed scientifically. Persons whose tears often cause a puffy face perhaps will identify with one subject who added this request on her questionnaire: "If you discover a way to cry like they do in the movies without getting a red nose and swollen eyes, let me know." Research may someday give us the answers to why some people experience the unpleasant physical effects of tears which Shakespeare in *Twelfth Night* referred to as "eye-offending brine."

How do you feel about emotional crying?

More females (73%) felt positive about crying than males (58%) in the study. Whether or not subjects in the study felt positive or negative about emotional crying did not affect the number of times they cried during the thirty-day recording period. Those who reported having negative feelings about crying recorded approximately the same crying frequency pattern as those who felt generally positive about emotional tears.

One subject considers crying a "very natural response," and another subject wrote, "We shouldn't fight what comes naturally." Other subjects also regarded crying as "perfectly normal for both men and women." Most subjects agreed with this response: "Great, everyone should cry a little."

Many of those who felt positive about crying commented on the feeling of relief and release that accompanies or follows crying. Some of the responses were:

"An excellent release of emotional tension and
   pressure."
"Gives a sense of relief."
"Safe way to vent frustration and anger."
"Relieves distress within."
"A much-needed outlet for stressful situations."

Others responded that not only was crying good for you, but that it is "not good to hold back tears," and crying is a "natural release that's stifled too much."

A good share of the subjects who view emotional crying as a positive response consider their tears as "eloquent messengers" that help them express their feelings and thoughts. "When words are hard to find, crying sometimes helps the words and thoughts to flow," wrote one subject. "It opens up avenues for family and friends to share problems," wrote another. Others responded that crying "helps show your feelings" and "shows you are a sensitive person." Or crying sometimes acts as a form of defense to tell others they have gone too far. In an argument, for example, tears can serve as a warning to stop—that enough is enough. Vassar psychologist Randolph Cornelius has suggested that "weeping appears to function as a signal, that bonds of attachment are in danger of being broken or have been broken and effectively reestablishes attachment because it is perceived to be involuntary and uncontrollable."[1]

"Crying makes me feel connected to myself," wrote one subject. Several others also reported that their emotional tears help them identify their own problems and gain insight similar to the woman who wrote, "Tears erupting over little things tell me I'm trying to cope with too much and make me stop and look at what I'm doing."

One of four responses which specifically mentioned male tears read: "I wish it was more acceptable for men to cry. It helps them to be more in touch with their tender selves." Another viewed crying as "a must for everyone—men included!!" Others felt "men should cry without feeling ashamed," since there is "nothing unmanly about it."

Twelve subjects wrote that crying is only acceptable in solitude, as they feel guilty, uneasy, or embarrassed when they or others cry in public. Seven reported they cry mainly when alone and seem to feel that crying is, as one subject put it, "a private and personal experience." Seventeen subjects feel crying is acceptable if kept in its proper place. "Crying is not socially acceptable in some circles," wrote one subject. Some indicated they were embarrassed when they cried over a personal problem or during an argument, but it was permissible to cry at a movie or over a sad story. A few said "crying is OK," except when it is used to gain pity or manipulate others. Several who expressed ambivalence about crying seemed to agree with the subject who wrote, "I'm torn by crying. It's a weakness and yet it's a strength to be able to cry."

Ten subjects who never or rarely cry indicated they wished they could. One man wrote, "I know it's OK to cry, but I never give myself permission." Another "had not felt safe enough to cry with someone in years," and several gave similar responses to the subject who wrote, "I wish I could cry, but I was taught not to show my emotions."

Ten percent of the females and 15% of the males in the study expressed negative feelings about emotional crying. Many who feel negative about crying consider weeping as "a sign of weakness," embarrassing, silly, irrational, too drastic, or manipulative. Several agreed with a subject who wrote, "Crying serves no real purpose except to control others." One said that crying upset her because it was a substitute for "assertively expressing" herself. A few subjects view crying negatively because their uncontrollable tears are bothersome. The two subjects who wrote, "It bothers me that I can't control my crying," and "I can't stop my tears—wish I didn't cry so easily" seemed to consider their tears as a troublesome nuisance. But their responses paled in contrast to this depressing response: "It has ruined my life."

Can you stop yourself from shedding emotional tears if you wish?

One of the reasons women visibly cry more often than men is that more men than women are able to stop their tears when they feel them coming. Sixty-eight percent of the men in the study reported they could stop their tears compared to 46% of the women who were able to hold back their tears. Also, men are more able than women to stop their tears when their eyes are already watery. Subjects who can stop themselves from crying do so by exerting some type of physical force such as gritting their teeth, clenching their jaw, biting their lip, or generally "bearing down." Others stop their tears by becoming angry, instead, or distracting themselves with other thoughts or a change of subject to avoid becoming emotionally involved.

One subject wrote that she could stop her tears but it is "painful" and she is "easily set off later." Another reported that because she came from a "stoic family" she usually tries to hold back her tears even though she feels "bottled up." Several subjects were able to control their tears sometimes and in certain situations. One subject wrote, "If left alone I can usually stop the tears, but if someone talks to me, I usually break down." Another subject stated, "When someone speaks to me in a sympathetic sense, I usually weep helplessly." Those who rarely are able to control their weeping reported they seldom receive much advance warning that they are about to weep and that the tears just come during an emotional situation. "Tears often flow from my eyes before I even know they are there," wrote one subject.

Can you make yourself cry with no external cause? If so, how do you do it?

While fewer females could voluntarily stop their tears, more women than men reported they could make themselves cry without an external cause. Only twenty women and two men reported being able to cry at will. Seventy-three percent of the women who could bring on their own tears did so by thinking sad thoughts: the death of a loved one, missing someone special, tragic events, or words to certain songs. Four subjects reported they could cry by just concentrating on making themselves cry; three subjects used theatrical training to induce tears in ways similar to this subject, who would "focus on a sad event, then center feelings on that event and state of mind."

How do you think others feel when you cry?

Men reported generally feeling better about the way others react and feel about their own crying than women. Sixty-three percent of the men and 49% of the women wrote that others were sympathetic when they cried. In addition, 13% of the men thought others had positive feelings when they cried compared to only 4% of the women. Thirty-five percent of the women and only 8% of the men thought others reacted with negative feelings when they shed tears. The remainder either felt neutral or did not know how others felt when they cried. Perhaps the reason men seem to get more positive feedback to their tears is that they are seen crying less often and thus possibly their tears are taken more seriously than female tears, which appear more frequently.

Those who thought others responded positively to their tears reported that their tears, and the feelings that caused the tears, were accepted and respected. Some described others' responses to their tears as sorry, concerned, willing to listen, understanding, closer, and sensitive. Several subjects thought others were supportive and consoling after noticing their tears. One person wrote that others often "feel like hugging me when I cry."

Many subjects thought their tears communicate something about their inner selves and make an important statement about themselves and their relationships with others:

"Shows that I'm comfortable with them and willing
　to share my inner thoughts with them."
"Shows I mean what I say."
"Breaks the emotional wall of isolation and shows a
　willingness to talk about what's bothering me."

Seven reported that they felt tears communicate a flaw in their character or make-up. They wrote that others think they are weak, childish, silly, crazy, over-emotional, or, as one subject wrote, "That I'm a big crybaby."

"I wish others wouldn't be so uncomfortable when I cry. They sometimes say, 'Don't cry' when I really feel like crying," wrote another subject.

A woman whose parents had taught her to stifle her emotions married a man who is indifferent to her tears and usually tries to control her weeping. Although she does cry when alone and feels it brings relief, this woman wrote, "Just once I'd like to feel what it's like to cry in front of someone and have them hold me and feel relieved afterward."

Many subjects reported that others reacted with feelings of inadequacy to their tears: embarrassed, uneasy, nervous, bewildererd, uncomfortable, awkward, flustered, helpless, confused. Several answers were similar to this subject's response: "They don't know what to say or do to make me feel better."

Some reported that others became angry, annoyed, frustrated, disturbed, or upset when they cried. Several women specifically mentioned that their husbands got angry. A few thought others felt "imposed upon" when they cried. Some subjects' family members had mixed responses to their tears: "My husband thinks I should be able to talk to him without crying, but he is usually sympathetic." "My dad says 'Don't cry,' then catches himself and says 'Cry.'"

Several subjects said everyone responds differently, depending on their attitude toward crying. One subject wrote, for example, that women felt sympathetic and men were uncomfortable when she cried.

In short, the results of our study, based on the responses in the questionnaire, indicate that most people feel better after crying and regard their own crying as a desirable, healthy release of tension.

And nineteenth century American writer Washington Irving goes so far as to say, "There is a sacredness in tears. They are not the mark of weakness, but of power. They speak more eloquently than ten thousand tongues. They are the messengers of overwhelming grief, of deep contrition, and of unspeakable love."

13

When Others Cry

The big lip and wat'ry eye
Tell me the rising storm is nigh.

Matthew Prior

One reason many older children and adults struggle so hard to
control their tears is that they anticipate and often get negative, unsupporting reactions from others. This lack of a positive reaction encourages the idea that crying indicates
weakness, vulnerability, and immaturity. For many persons
this idea has become so ingrained that they eventually do not
or cannot allow themselves to shed emotional tears, no matter
how deep the pain or strong the emotion.

"Don't Cry, Baby"

Because most adults learned in childhood that they should not
cry or show anger or act fearful, they teach their own and
other children the same suppressing pattern of denial of feelings, writes Harvey Jackins in his book, *The Human Side of
Human Beings.* Instead of being allowed to discharge the
distress felt after a hurtful experience, children are taught
that their natural reaction upsets those around them. Jackins
gives examples of how adults try to stop children's crying by
attempting to comfort or distract them:

"There, there, don't cry, it's all right, don't cry."

Others use anger and threats to try to control crying.

"Shut up! You stop your crying or I'll give you
something to cry about."

"All right, son, get a grip on yourself! No use crying.
Crying doesn't do any good."

And still others resort to guilt.

"Please stop that crying. You're making Mama feel
bad."

Regardless of whether adults kindly or cruelly tell a child
not to cry, children get the message that they should suppress
their feelings and their tears. Even many lullabies include
"don't cry" messages. The natural healing process of expression will not be distorted if children are raised in an environment of "caretaking adults who are . . . able to be relaxed
and undistressed when baby is distressed . . . ," Jackins
writes.[1]

Much has been written about how to respond to infant
crying, and therefore I won't discuss it at any length. However, it is important to respond to infant crying by picking up
babies, holding them, and giving them as much attention as
you have the energy to give. Crying is a baby's primary
method of communication, and it is important that the baby
learns that someone will respond to his or her distress. A
secure and emotionally well-nourished baby is preferable to
an infant who feels helpless and abandoned.

I believe older children should also be allowed to cry. If
their crying is annoying you or interfering with your activity,
you can take them to their room or somewhere else, where
they can finish crying without bothering you or others. When
my daughter was four years old, she went through a period in
which she occasionally carried on like one of the Whiners on
"Saturday Night Live," sometimes while I was on the phone.
If her crying continued after I had responded and felt reasonably certain that nothing drastic was causing her tears, I
would take her to her room where she could cry as loud and as
long as she wanted, without interfering with my phone conversation. I feel she has the right to cry, but I also have the
right to talk on the phone. On the other hand, you do not
want to punish children by banishing them to their room

every time they cry, or you will teach them that crying is bad and should be suppressed. Dr. Aletha Solter's book, *The Aware Baby: A New Approach to Parenting* (Shining Press, 1984) discusses in great detail the role crying plays in a child's development.

When Others Cry

As I mentioned in Chapter Twelve, a number of subjects in our crying behavior study reported that others' reactions to their crying included embarrassment, inadequacy, anger, frustration, or disgust. Responses from those in the study who felt negative when others cried were often short and direct: guilty, horrible, bad, bewildered, helpless, awkward, and powerless. A few interpreted tears as a loss of control. Others thought tears were often used to manipulate, as one subject wrote, "I feel like they're using me with their tears." Several subjects reported that their feelings depend on the situation and who is crying. "I feel consoling if a woman cries; I'm uncomfortable when a man cries. It seems more severe," wrote one subject. Another responded, "It depends on who's crying and why. I feel sympathetic unless they're crying for a recurring problem and they haven't tried to amend it."

Several subjects indicated they would like to respond in a supportive manner when someone else cries, but they simply do not know what to say or do. Women indicated they felt only slightly more sympathetic and less negative when someone else cries than the men in the study. Eighty percent of the women and 74% of the men reported feeling sympathetic when others cried.

Many who responded to others' crying with sympathy and compassion encouraged the person to cry, and one expressed feeling a desire to console and help. The following responses represent the way many subjects respond when others cry:

"Feel like hugging them."
"Want to comfort them, yet let them cry."

"Protective."

"Glad they're letting their feelings out."

"Rush of love and compassion."

Those of us who feel that crying is a natural way to relieve stress can help lessen the social taboo that surrounds crying by helping others learn to accept their own and others' tears by responding to crying in a sensitive and positive way.

Actually, very little has been written on how to respond when another cries except in literature dealing with grief and hospitalized patients. However, these suggestions have general utility. This material covers not only what to say and do when others cry but also—equally important—what *not* to do and say.

Grief

Much has been written about how to help others through the mourning of a loved one. Weizman and Kamm acknowledge how difficult it is for the bereaved to find "someone you can talk to as much as you need to talk, to be able to cry without being embarrassed, and to be able to be real." A remark such as "'You must be strong' usually means: 'Don't cry; I can't bear to see you cry.' Tears are a physiological as well as an emotional release for grief. Crying has nothing to do with strength: it is an expression of feelings. . . . It is most important for family and friends to understand the mourning process and to give open permission to share feelings. Encourage the bereaved to talk about the deceased, talk about their pain, anger, sorrow, and let the tears flow unashamedly." They recommend others show their support with simple and sincere remarks such as: "I know you hurt deeply."[2]

Grief is usually associated with death, but as Ira Tanner wrote in his book *The Gift of Grief,* "Grief is reaction to any *loss*" whether it be death, divorce, health, job, self-esteem, or even the loss of familiar surroundings when one moves to another location.[3]

Anxiety

People experiencing anxiety often seem to be on the verge of tears but need their own and others' permission to release their tears. In their article in the January, 1976, issue of *The Canadian Nurse,* authors Abigail McGreevy and Judy Van Heukelem suggest how nurses can help patients who need to cry. When nurses sense a patient is about to cry, they can verbally encourage the crying by saying, "You look like you need to cry" or "It's all right to cry" or "Go ahead and let it all out"; or nonverbally by touching the patient softly and communicating with tone of voice, relaxed posture, and an accepting attitude conveying that the patient has their undivided attention. They also urge nurses to be aware of the difference between the patient who needs complete privacy to cry and the patient who says he or she wants privacy but indicates nonverbally their need to be with someone who understands.

When a patient cries, McGreevy and Van Heukelem recommend staying quietly nearby, maintaining a posture of warm acceptance but refraining from initiating or encouraging conversation. Nurses may cry along with the patient as long as they remain objective and do not lose control. After the patient stops crying, a willingness to listen with questions such as "Is there some way I can help?" will communicate respect for his or her feelings and reassure the patient that the tears are not burdensome. The authors also recommend that nurses be prepared for the next meeting with the patient who has cried, which may be strained. They should convey that there is no need for the patient to feel ill-at-ease for having openly cried.[4]

In a 1971 study of twenty-five nursing students' reactions to crying patients, Fred and Brenda Forster found that their responses generally cut off patient communication and offered only superficial reassurance. The students showed indirect disapproval or unwillingness to get involved in several ways. They

- denied the problem by saying "There's nothing to worry about."

- changed the subject or indicated a willingness to converse only at a "chit-chat" level.
- belittled the patient's reaction by saying "everyone" has the same or worse problem.
- offered a ready-made solution or distraction: "Should I turn on the TV?"
- ignored clues about person's underlying needs.
- never mentioned noticing the person was crying or seemed upset.[5]

Ways to Respond

An old Armenian proverb suggests, "Tears are a language; only he who weeps understands them." Therefore, to tell someone who is crying "I know exactly how you feel" is often counterproductive. Remarks such as this often tend to make the crying person feel misunderstood, angry, and usually anything but better. Too many memories, feelings, and perceptions are often behind whatever brought the tears, and such shallow remarks often alienate the crying person even though the comforter is trying to give support and show genuine concern. Leo Buscaglia said it well: "You can never understand someone else's tears. Tears are very lonely and very private. You can't say 'I know *exactly* why you're crying.'"

Crying seems to be a more satisfying release when others respond in a warm, positive manner without being overly solicitous. It is important to be perceptive regarding others' tears. Some may want to be held, while others prefer to be alone and have time to think. Some may want a friend to just quietly be there, while others may want to talk after they stop crying.

While there may be individuals who occasionally shed tears with no real emotion behind them simply to manipulate others, I feel that very few tears are shed in this way, since few persons are able to elicit their own tears. Everyone should be aware, however, that they may encounter someone who occasionally uses tears to deceive others. Perhaps the best way to discourage this is to confront the person directly with your doubts.

Several forms of therapy actively encourage crying as part of the healing process. Reevaluation counseling, or cocounseling, founded by Harvey Jackins and others, provides a relationship in which two persons take turns being the counseled and the counselor. They are encouraged to release distress through tears, anger, and talking through their repressed hurts.

Obviously, as I said earlier, if someone who cries frequently also shows signs of physical or mental illness, he or she should be encouraged to seek professional help. But most crying is a natural and normal way of responding to stress and emotion, and we all can play a role in helping others to feel reasonably comfortable when they weep. Considering the positive way in which the majority of the subjects in our study reported feeling when someone else cries, it seems that people need not worry about their crying and how others will respond. Overall, it appears that most adults view weeping as an acceptable natural response to emotional stress to which they respond with sympathy and compassion.

14

Do Animals Shed Emotional Tears?

*It is a curious thing that man is
the only creature that weeps.*

Ashley Montagu

Most scientists concur with Raymond E. Record's opinion in his book *Physiology of the Human Eye and Visual System* that "Psychogenic tearing is unique to the human. It is never seen in lower animals."[1] Most zoologists acknowledge that many animals whine or cry out when they are in stressful situations or in pain, but, they insist, animals do not shed emotional tears—except perhaps on extremely rare occasions. Despite this conviction, a few reports during the last century of nonhuman animals shedding emotional tears have led some scholars to suggest that the process of emotional tearing may have also evolved in animals other than humans.

Some Scientists Say Animals Cry Tears

Several reports of animals shedding emotional tears—or what were interpreted as emotional tears—in the scientific literature cannot be ignored. In the *Expression of the Emotions in Man and Animals,* Charles Darwin writes:

> The Indian elephant is known sometimes to weep. Sir E. Tennent, in describing these which he saw captured and bound in Ceylon, says, some "lay motionless on the ground, with no other indication of suffering than the tears which suffused their eyes and flowed incessantly."

Speaking of another elephant he says, "When overpowered and made fast, his grief was most affecting; his violence sank to utter prostration, and he lay on the ground, uttering choking cries, with tears trickling down his cheeks." In the Zoological Gardens the keeper of the Indian elephants positively asserts that he has several times seen tears rolling down the face of the old female, when distressed by the removal of the young one.

Darwin's attempts to obtain further documentation of the weeping of the Indian elephant were unsuccessful. His request for information on the emotional tearing of elephants from one of his colleagues in Ceylon failed to confirm earlier reports:

> . . . in consequence [I] received a letter from the Rev. Mr. Glenie, who, with others, kindly observed for me a herd of recently captured elephants. These, when irritated, screamed violently; . . . but . . . never . . . contracted the muscles round the eyes. Nor did they shed tears; and the native hunters asserted they had never observed elephants weeping.[2]

In 1925 Cecil Reynolds wrote that dogs and wolves shed tears when they are "on the verge of exhaustion," and, thus, "not much good for . . . hunting; by common consent, he runs at the rear of the pack and is urged and guided by his neighbors. They instinctively know that he is a good warrior and will recover, but is in need of forebearance."[3]

According to two biological scientists, the tears of seals and sea otters increase during stressful periods. In his 1966 book, *Grey Seal, Common Seal*, field naturalist Ronald M. Lockley writes:

> If we examine the eye of a seal we find . . . the eyeball is lubricated by an oily grease or tears which continually flow from a duct in the inner corner of the eye; in man this duct is connected with the nose, and our lubricatory tears flow internally—unless we are moved emotionally to copious weeping, when they flow both ways. But the seal has no nasolacrymal duct, which explains why, out

of the water, seal cheeks are always wet with tears—and these tears can flow more copiously, as in man, when the seal is alarmed, frightened, or otherwise agitated.[4]

Georg W. Stellar, who specialized in the study of marine mammals, writes of the sea otter: "I have sometimes deprived females of their young on purpose, sparing the lives of the mothers, and they would weep over their affliction like human beings."[5]

"Red tears" shed by laboratory rats have also been the focus of research. The rats secreted a red-brown liquid from their eyes when experiencing acute stress in a study conducted by John E. Harkness and Marcella D. Ridgway, published in *Laboratory Animal Science.* The "tears" appeared to be one of several exaggerated adaptive responses to stressors—such as immobilization—with which the rat cannot readily cope. After their front limbs were restrained with adhesive tape, the rats were placed in deep wood chip bedding. Within several minutes, a reddish-brown substance appeared around their eyes following a period of kicking, squeaking, jumping, rolling and running backwards. For about two hours the restrained rats shed tears, rapidly at first then slowly decreasing. While the tears were flowing, the rats lay quietly except for an occasional thrash. After several hours some of the rats learned to walk on their rear feet and the others eventually adapted and found ways to move in spite of their immobilized front limbs. The relationship between the excretion of red-brown tears (chromodacryorrhea) from the rats' Harderian glands and the secretion of tears from the human lacrimal gland in response to emotional stress remains to be explored.[6]

Dian Fossey, a scientist with a Ph.D. in animal behavior from Cambridge University, is known for her long-term observations of the mountain gorilla. In her book, *Gorillas in the Mist,* she reports that she has seen Coco, a three-year-old female gorilla in captivity, cry while staring out a window at her former jungle home. "Suddenly she began to sob and shed actual tears, something I had never seen a gorilla do before or since," Fossey writes.[7]

Elaine Morgan, author of *The Descent of Woman* and *The Aquatic Ape,* devotes a portion of her books to her proposal that humans are not the only animals that produce emotional tears. While all mammals have tear glands, the human is the only primate and seems to be the only terrestrial mammal (except for the Indian elephant) that sheds emotional tears, she says. Morgan proposes that emotional tears are one of many similarities linking our evolution to marine and terrestrial animals that acquired aquatic features during a period when their ancestors lived or spent much time in the sea. In her books she argues in support of the aquatic theory of evolution, a hypothesis first proposed by Alister Hardy. The theory suggests that the ancestors of *homo sapiens* were land apes who were forced to adapt to water when much of their territory was engulfed by the sea; they emigrated to the water to find food and escape predators. Later, the theory proposes, predecessors of the human returned to the land and once again became terrestrial mammals with new intrinsic aquatic adaptation. Many human traits such as the presence of subcutaneous fat, lack of body hair, and presence of tears—which are different from other primates and similar to some marine animals and animals who once were marine animals—are presented in support of the theory of the aquatic evolution of the human race.

One trait some aquatic and ex-aquatic animals have in common is that "from somewhere or other in the vicinity of the eyes or nose or beak a saline liquid emerges and flows," Morgan says. She suggests that some marine and "former" marine animals shed not just continuous and irritant tears, but, like humans, also shed emotional tears.

Morgan and other proponents of the aquatic theory of evolution propose that the Indian elephant may be one ex-aquatic animal that spent millions of years in the sea before returning to land. After reading Darwin's accounts of elephants shedding tears, Morgan wrote she was surprised to later learn that elephants have no lacrimal glands, but Harderian glands, which have tubes that open on the surface of the nictitating membrane (a transparent inner eyelid present in birds and some animals that draws over the eye to moisten and protect it). She asked the elephant keeper at the Zoological Gardens in London if he'd ever seen elephants cry. He replied that they shed tears if they're upset.

She supports her theory with Lockley's and Stellar's reports of seals and sea otters weeping for apparently emotional reasons, and with the accounts of marine birds and reptiles excreting tears to remove the irritation of the saltwater both internally and externally. She cited Smith's report of an increase in the albatross' nasal tears during periods of arousal. "Nasal dripping was observed to occur when the birds had been fighting with each other, during ritual dancing, or even the excitement of feeding time."

Morgan writes, "Tears of marine birds flow freely in emotional situations as well as following a disturbance of the salt balance. . . . I believe they do shed tears. I think we use our lacrimal glands, the seagull uses his nasal glands, and the elephant uses his Harderian glands; but I think we all shed tears."[8, 9]

What Animal Experts Say

The claims that nonhuman animals shed emotional tears must not be ignored, but it may be premature to state that nonhuman animals normally shed emotional tears until more scientific research is conducted. Part of the problem is our inability to accurately assess emotion in animals with whom we cannot communicate. (We have enough trouble communicating accurately with others in our own species.) In any case, this suggestion must be evaluated cautiously, since people have a tendency to romanticize their feelings about animals by anthropomorphizing them. On the other hand, there is also an opposite tendency to assume that animals cannot possibly do those things which humans can do. Also, the way animals behave in the wild and in captivity may be quite different. Furthermore, rare events do occur in nature. For example, some forms of bamboo produce flowers only once every century. While it may be hard to observe this, it does occur. All these factors must be taken into account when considering the question of whether other animals shed emotional tears.

In an attempt to learn more about emotional crying in other animals, I contacted several veterinarians and animal trainers who have worked extensively with seals, dolphins, and whales at Sea World in Orlando, Florida, the Seaquarium in Miami, Florida, Marineland in Los Angeles, California, and the Como Park Zoo in St. Paul, Minnesota. I even spoke with the trainer of Salty, the star sea lion at Miami Seaquarium. These experienced sea animal trainers and veterinarians all stated that seals, dolphins, and whales secrete a watery mucus to protect their eyes from sea water. The overflow of tears due to the lack of a drainage system may have been misconstrued as emotional tears. No one I contacted said they had ever seen seals or other sea animals shed emotional tears, nor do they believe the animals shed tears except to lubricate and protect their eyes.

However, Brian Davies, an animal protectionist and executive director of the International Fund for Animal Welfare, reports seals do shed tears over their dead offspring. He wrote, "I have seen female seals beside pups killed by seal hunters . . . tears have rolled from their eyes. I believe they are tears of emotion, because other seals in the immediate area have not been shedding tears which should have been the case if environment was the immediate trigger of this action."[10]

We sent questionnaires to ten major zoological parks in North America and other zoologists, breeders, and trainers requesting information about emotional tears in nonhuman animals. The two principal questions were (1) Have you ever seen nonhuman animals shed emotional tears? and (2) Do you know of any documented evidence of nonhuman animals shedding emotional tears?

By the time this book was ready to be published, we had received replies from Saul Kitchener, director of the San Francisco Zoological Park, R. M. McNoman, assistant curator of mammals, Bronx Zoo, G. Styfer, overseer at the Toronto Zoological Park, Donald L. Jansen, DVM, associate veterinarian at the San Diego Wild Animal Park, and Sanford

Friedman, curator and chairman of the mammal department at the Brookfield Zoological Park in Illinois. All responded "no" to both questions.

Frederick A. King, director of the Yerkes Primate Center in Atlanta, Georgia, reported that he had never seen any type of monkey shed emotional tears, nor had his colleagues. "A survey of five experienced primate scientists at the Yerkes Center revealed that none of them had seen primate emotional tears in any species of prosimians, monkeys or great apes," King added to the questionnaire.

Ian Douglas-Hamilton, who has done extensive studies of African elephants replied, "I cannot say that I observed emotional tears in African elephants, although I have seen tears appear when they have been shot or wounded. It is possible that these may be related to emotion, but I am sorry to say I really do not have enough observation in this to say one way or the other."

We received only one partially positive response on our questionnaires. As we were working on this chapter, the Franzen Brothers Circus set up their tents in Sandstone, Minnesota, near Langseth's home for a one-night performance. As the show's Indian elephant, Okha, was giving rides between her appearances in the ring, Langseth noticed tears running down the elephant's face and asked the man leading her what had caused the tears. He replied he wasn't sure why she shed tears. He also said Okha was a one-man elephant and suggested Langseth contact Okha's trainer and co-owner of the circus, Wayne Franzen. In response to a request for information about Okha's tears, Franzen wrote, "An elephant does shed tears. However, I have no idea as to what emotional connection may be involved. Okha does shed a tear when being scolded sometimes and squints her eyes much like a child."

Other Reports of Animals' Tears

Although nearly all of the animal experts I contacted failed to corroborate the theory of emotional tears in animals proposed by some scientists, I have received dozens of reports from persons who claim to have seen animals shed tears during stressful periods. These letters came to me during the past five years in response to interviews or seminars I had given about our crying research, in which I had usually stated that emotional tears are one of the few things that distinguish us from other animals.

For example, after a St. Paul woman had read an article in a Minneapolis newspaper in 1982 about the tear research, she wrote to tell me about an ancient Mexican breed of dog called Xoloitzcuintli (Xolo) that "does indeed cry real tears when it is upset emotionally." She suggested I contact a Xolo breeder in Coyoacan, Mexico. I wrote, asking if these dogs actually cry tears when upset. The breeder, who has worked with Xolos for almost thirty years, responded, "Xolos have been known to have tears but . . . (it) . . . is not usual." She did not write that she personally had seen these dogs shed tears.

In an attempt to verify the claims about this smooth-skinned dog, which is often referred to as a "hot water bottle" because its body temperature is 104°F (40°C), we also wrote to two experienced breeders in the United States. One from Massachusetts replied that she had not seen Xolos, also called Mexican hairless, shed tears and added that they often get a lot of "junk" in their eyes that may look like tears.

The secretary of The American Hairless Dog Club and The American Chinese Crested Club, who has raised and shown these dogs for twenty-five years, reported her "Xolo bitch . . . would cry if she did wrong and I scolded her. When she whelped, and the vet had a hard time pulling the puppies, she never uttered a word, but tears ran down her face." This New Jersey breeder also told of one of her Mexican hairless dogs who cries when she is picked up at the airport after having been away from home for several months to be bred. "When I . . . take her from her carrier she will cry tears all over me—happy to see me." She added that her Chihuahua, American Chinese crested, and Peruvian Inca orchid also shed tears when left or scolded.

Shortly after an article on our tear and crying research appeared in *USA Today* in 1983, I received two letters from persons who claimed to have seen Boston terriers shed emotional tears. A woman in Bellingham, Washington, wrote, "I used to know a dog, a toy Boston bull, belonging to friends, who, when he was scolded, would go under a table and cry, tears running down his face." I wrote to the woman and asked for further documentation such as written statements from other witnesses or a veterinarian but received no reply.

A retired science teacher from Coffeyville, Kansas, sent another report of the same breed shedding emotional tears. She wrote, "I saw a Boston bull terrier pup with tears rolling from its eyes and dropping off, lots of tears. It was in a crate waiting to be shipped by express from an Iowa lake resort station. This was many years ago, but I have never forgotten that weeping puppy. Talking to it only made it cry harder. I had never before and have not again seen an animal shed tears, but this one did." (It is interesting to note that three of the reports of nonhuman animal emotional tears—the bound Indian elephant, the immobilized rats, the crated Boston terrier—all occurred when the animals were restrained in some manner.)

We sent questionnaires to eight breeders of Boston terriers throughout the United States. Of the six who responded, four replied that they had seen Boston terriers shed emotional tears and added names of other owners to contact who also claim to have seen their own Boston terrier or know of one shedding emotional tears. One breeder wrote that terriers shed emotional tears when one "just talks sympathetic to them." She told of one weeping episode that occurred when the owners had to find a new home for their Boston terrier. Another aged, sickly Boston terrier reportedly had shed tears when the owner sat it on the table to say good-bye before bringing it to the vet to have it put to sleep. One owner said their dog had shed tears when the owner swatted it with a newspaper.

A couple who have raised Boston terriers for twenty-six years from Northridge, California, reported that one of their male Boston terriers had shed tears on three occasions. The first incident happened when she returned from a ten-day stay in the hospital. The dog "jumped on the bed, and as I reached over to pet him and talk to him—tears streamed from his eyes. I had a new silk coverlet on the bed—the tear stains never washed out," she wrote. The other two teary incidents also involved pets being left by their owners.

In an article about our research in the November, 1984, issue of *Parade,* reporter Sara Brzowsky wrote about the reports we had received of animals shedding emotional tears. During the following weeks I received over two dozen more letters from people all over the country who had seen animals shed emotional tears. As I opened letter after letter with accounts of weeping animals, I began to feel that I must be one of the few persons who had never seen animals shed emotional tears. Present and former dog owners of eight breeds other than Boston terrier and Mexican hairless sent accounts of isolated or multiple incidents in which they had personally seen dogs shed tears:

- A woman from Tennessee reported seeing her son's Pomeranian, temporarily left in her care, shed tears while confined in the bathroom by a gate. She wrote: "Once, as I passed the bathroom door, I realized he was making a strange sound, not the usual snoring sound. He was laying at the door with his head resting in his paws and big tears were rolling down his face. His whole body was shaking as he sobbed, the sounds were doubtless coming from deep within."
- According to a Texas woman, her black Labrador wept for weeks after their other dog was run over by a car. She wrote: "I found her lying on top of the spot I had buried the other dog. She wasn't making a sound, but big, huge tears were rolling down her face. Each morning she would be on top of the grave, crying."
- Another account read: "I distinctly remember when I was about thirteen, sitting and sobbing one night. I was home alone with our English bull terrier, who was sitting directly in front of me, and as I cried, tears rolled down his face."
- We also received reports of a Pekinese who shed tears and sobbed when her owner scolded her in a loud voice, a Chihauhau-terrier mix that would cry every time the dog was told in an angry voice to get into its box, a miniature

poodle who "weeps real tears of dejection and regret," a German shepherd who shed tears following surgery, along with accounts from others who did not give specific breeds or incidents but just wrote to tell us they had witnessed dogs shedding emotional tears.

In addition to the accounts of canine tears, we received the following reports of other weeping animals.

- I received four letters from persons claiming that their cats had cried tears when upset. One woman from Virginia wrote that her cat had shed tears when she held and stroked him after he had been gone for a few days or when she has been extremely busy and not taken the time to show him any affection. Another woman from Virginia reported her cat "cries real tears when it is injured or badly frightened."

- Several letters from persons with rural backgrounds reported witnessing tears shed by farm animals about to be slaughtered or after being separated from their young. A woman from Washington wrote: "You don't have to go to . . . zoos to find these tears. I grew up on a farm in Minnesota and saw many, many tears shed by cows when their calves were taken from them. . . . All day long the mother would call for her calf, tears streaming down her face."

- A California woman told of a hog-butchering incident from her childhood in Connecticut in which five or six pigs were lined up in a roped area in a neighbor's backyard. She wrote: "They were quiet until the first one was slaughtered (its throat slit and then hung up to bleed to death). The three things I remember about the pigs in line were their reluctance to move (had to be dragged), their screaming (a frightful sound), and their tears—large, round tears falling from their eyes and down their faces."

- A Louisiana woman wrote of a childhood experience in which she had watched a lamb about to be butchered by her uncle: "He tied it up, and it started whimpering like a baby, and big tears rolled out its eyes, wetting his face. I said, 'It's crying, Uncle. How can you kill it?' He said sheep and lambs always cry when they know they are going to die."

- "I had a horse that cried emotional tears once," wrote a Utah woman. "I was riding in the hills behind my house on a moonlit night and got off and walked with him and talked gently. He started crying and whinnied very softly bumping my arm with his nose. I started crying, too. It never happened again, but we were never again in a situation that seemed so close."
- A man from Georgia wrote: "While reading your article about tears, I remembered watching a loggerhead turtle lay her eggs on the beach at Jekyll Island. Of course, we couldn't see her eyes while she was digging the hole but after she started to lay her eggs we turned the flashlight on. At first her eyes were dry, but she shed tears as she progressed. Whether they were emotional or painful tears, I don't know but thought you might be interested."
- Another person challenged the notion that emotional crying is unique to the human in a letter telling of a pet kangaroo in Australia who had shed tears when its young mistress was ill and could not come out to play. Years later when the kangaroo's joey was attacked and killed by a pack of wild dogs, the grieving mother wailed and shed tears for days, she wrote.

Lack of Documented Scientific Evidence

I have asked several owners to provide further evidence of animals shedding emotional tears, either by videotaping the episode or obtaining a testimony from a veterinarian or other animal expert. To date, I have received none. When I asked several small animal veterinarians if they had ever observed dogs shedding emotional tears, they all told me they had never witnessed psychogenic tearing in any animal and added that they felt all animals' tears were due to eye irritation or inflammation.

Reports of these few animals shedding emotional tears have not yet convinced me that nonhuman animals routinely shed emotional tears as a normal response to strong emotional stress. These anecdotal reports suggest, however, that there may be some individuals of some species that have on occasion shed emotional tears. It will be very important during the next few years to obtain documentation of this type of crying in healthy animals including videotape evidence. Until evidence of other animals shedding emotional tears is well documented, I will continue to maintain that emotional tearing generally occurs only in humans. I agree with Montagu's view that "the shedding of tears as an accompaniment to emotional distress has been attributed to other animals. . . . The truth, however, appears to be that while some of these animals may on occasion exhibit the evidences of tears, this occurs very seldom, and is the exception rather than the rule. . . . Psychic weeping is not known to occur as a normal function in any animal other than man."[11]

15

Future Research

If we would have new knowledge,
we must get a whole world of new questions.

Susan K. Langer

Greater knowledge of the lacrimal system is necessary before we can fully understand the overall cyring process. As far as I know, our tear research at SPRMC is the only work presently being done on the biochemistry of emotional tears. Studies on the psychological and behavioral aspects of emotional crying have increased in the last decade, but scientists are just now beginning to focus their research on the biological aspects of crying.

New Tear Research Groups

In November, 1984, tear researchers from all over the world participated in the First International Tear Film Symposium in Lubbock, Texas—the first symposium ever held specifically on the subject of tears. Clinicians and laboratory researchers gathered to exchange information and establish bridges of communication primarily on the physiological function and disorders of the tear film. I presented two papers at this symposium: one based on our research on hormones in the lacrimal system and another on emotional tears and crying. This was the only paper presented on emotional tearing. Hopefully, at future conferences, others will contribute to this new field. An International Society of Dacryology was organized during the symposium, which is dedicated to the study of tears.

I recently helped form and serve as Research Director of the St. Paul-Ramsey Dry Eye and Tear Research Center. This center, headed by SPRMC ophthalmologist Dr. J. Daniel Nelson, is the only one in the country devoted entirely to both physical and emotional tearing problems. Dr. Marlin Wiemer serves as consulting psychologist for the center. Many people from around the country have asked us for help with a variety of tearing problems including traditional ophthalmologic disorders such as dry eye syndrome and less studied emotional crying problems. These include the inability to cry, excessive crying that interferes with daily functioning, uncontrollable weeping while eating, and even uncontrollable tearing while urinating or defecating, just to mention a few.

Many More Questions on Tears

The solution to many of these crying problems depends upon future research into the emotional tearing process. Of particular importance is research on the human lacrimal gland and tears, looking for chemicals which regulate the production and secretion of tears. While prolactin, ACTH, acetylcholine, leucine enkephalin, substance P, and perhaps androgens may fall into this category, they certainly do not constitute the entire list. Understanding which hormones exert permissive control over weeping may help us to understand why some individuals seem to have a low threshold for crying and cry frequently while others cry rarely if at all. Furthermore, if the key hormones that promote tear production and secretion can be identified, then increasing their concentrations in the lacrimal gland may provide a treatment for certain types of dry eye disorders. As a part of these studies, it will be important to compare the tear and serum concentrations of these substances in individuals with dry eye syndrome, those with an inability to cry, and those individuals who suffer from excessive crying. Tear concentrations will be of special interest, since they may more accurately reflect the hormonal status of the lacrimal gland. Because serum prolactin levels increase so dramatically during pregnancy, it will also be worthwhile to scientifically determine if crying frequency increases markedly during pregnancy and if dry eye symptoms decrease.

Equally important will be research on the human lacrimal gland and tears, looking for chemical correlates of stress. Prolactin, ACTH, growth hormone and beta-endorphin are released from the pituitary in response to stress. Also the catecholamines such as epinephrine, norepinephrine and dopamine are important. However, it is possible if not probable, that the key biochemicals associated with emotional stress and emotion have not even been discovered yet. What better place to look for these substances than in emotional tears, the body's natural excretory response to emotional stress! Perhaps by studying tears we will discover not only why we cry but also what is the biochemical basis of emotion.

Even in the area of anatomy, there is much to be done. Differences between the male and female rat lacrimal glands have been reported and are thought to be due to hormonal differences between the sexes. It is not known if hormonally-induced anatomical and/or biochemical differences exist between the human male and female lacrimal glands. Also the lacrimal gland sits very near the brain. The pituitary gland, which also is located near the brain, receives direct chemical regulatory signals from the brain separate from its neural innervation. Is it possible that the lacrimal gland also receives direct chemical signals from the brain?

We have recently identified a group of more than ten children who range in age from one to fifteen years who have never shed emotional tears. These children appear to have neither familial dysautonomia nor dry eye syndrome, and yet they are progressing through childhood without ever weeping. This is certainly unusual and should be carefully studied. Why do these children not cry tears, and what consequences, if any, does the absence of emotional tears have on their health and development?

And Questions on Crying

Crying behavior research is also needed to answer a variety of questions. In their book, *Grief and Mourning in Cross-Culture Perspective,* Paul Rosenblatt and his associates report that there is a degree of similarity in crying behavior following the death of a loved one in various cultures around the world.[1] Other cross-cultural studies are needed to determine if crying behavior for reasons other than bereavement varies markedly in different cultural or ethnic groups. For example, Dr. Juan Murube del Castillo, perhaps the most knowledgeable writer on dacryology, has observed that the Rif tribe of northern Morocco does not shed emotional tears. If this is so, then we may learn much from studying these people and the way they experience, express, and adapt to emotional stress. Even among larger ethnic groups such as the English, Irish, Hungarian, Chinese, Italian, Norwegian, German, or Mexican populations there may be significant differences in crying behavior. Yet not even crying frequency has been studied scientifically in these groups. We recently sent information on our crying behavior study to a Hungarian researcher who plans to duplicate our study for cross-cultural comparison.

It would also be of interest to examine crying behavior in different disorders such as premenstrual syndrome or in the affective disorders of mania and depression. While notions of greatly increased crying in these disorders are held by some, documented evidence of increased crying frequency is scarce.

Dr. Margaret Crepeau's work suggests a possible connection between crying behavior and stress-related disorders such as ulcers and colitis. This research needs to be expanded so that we can determine to what extent crying behavior affects our susceptibility to stress-related disorders. It is also important to try to measure changes that occur along with crying in stress-related parameters such as blood pressure, heart rate, or serum levels of ACTH and cortisol. Can we demonstrate that crying reduces the effects of stress on the body?

As discussed in an earlier chapter, our data reveals no genetic component to crying frequency. However, no one has investigated to what extent crying behavior is learned by observing the crying behavior of parents and older siblings.

The first conference devoted specifically to crying behavior was held during the 1981 annual meeting of the American Psychological Association in Washington, D.C. Dr. Thomas Scheff, a University of California-Santa Barbara sociology professor and author of *Catharsis in Healing, Drama, and Ritual* (University of California Press, 1979), chaired the conference. Other panel members—all researchers on some aspect of crying—were Margaret Crepeau who presented her work on crying in relationship to ulcers and colitis; Paul Rosenblatt, University of Minnesota family social science professor who discussed his findings on grief over death and separation; and myself. Hopefully, similar conferences will be held in the future to encourage more crying behavior research.

Finally, it is important to determine to what extent emotional tearing occurs in other animals and, if possible, to obtain videotape evidence of crying in nonhuman species. Surely, if this occurs to the extent that my mail indicates, we can document crying in at least some of these animals.

Scientific investigations into emotional tears and crying have only just begun. Tears may hold the key to the mystery of human emotion and help us to understand our feelings, which are so important to each of us but about which we know so little. A multidisciplinary approach to the study of crying will do much to bring understanding to this neglected aspect of being human.

In the meantime, we are continuing to compile data. You can help with this future research yourself, if you wish, by copying and completing the questionnaire in the appendix, and sending it to us.

Appendix

Questionnaire

Your answers to the following questions will help guide the direction of future research on tears and crying behavior. Even if you seldom or never cry, we would appreciate your responses. It is not necessary to sign the questionnaire.

Sex: M   F

Date of birth:

Nation of family origin:

Ethnicity:
_____ White
_____ Black
_____ Hispanic
_____ Native American
_____ Asian
_____ Other

(Permission is given to reproduce this questionnaire.)

Religion:

Your family's average yearly income:
_____ Less than $10,000
_____ $10,000 to $20,000
_____ $20,000 to $35,000
_____ $35,000 to $50,000
_____ $50,000 to $65,000
_____ Over $65,000

Do you wear glasses?
Soft contact lenses?
Hard contact lenses?
Eye color:
_____ Brown
_____ Blue
_____ Hazel
_____ Green
_____ Gray
_____ Other

Are you currently taking any medication, including birth control pills? Please specify.

Do you have any medical illnesses? (Asthma, colitis, ulcers, high blood pressure, allergies, diabetes, thyroid problems, etc.)

Do you have any psychiatric illnesses (mania, depression, etc.)?

Do you have a problem with tears? _____ Yes _____ No
(If yes, please specify.)
_____ Dry eyes

(Permission is given to reproduce this questionnaire.)

_____ Excessive emotional crying
_____ Other (Please specify)

On the average, how many times a month do you shed emotional tears (including episodes where your eyes become watery as well as those where tears flow out of your eyes)?   Please give a number.

How do you generally feel after crying?
_____ Better
_____ No different
_____ Worse

Do you ever feel the need to cry but are unable to?
_____ Never
_____ Sometimes
_____ Usually
_____ Always

Can you stop yourself from shedding emotional tears if you wish?
_____ Never
_____ Sometimes
_____ Usually
_____ Always

Can you make yourself cry with no external cause?
_____ Never
_____ Sometimes
_____ Usually
_____ Always

(Permission is given to reproduce this questionnaire.)

If you have ever been pregnant, did you notice that your crying frequency

_____ did not change

_____ increased

_____ decreased during your pregnancy?

Is your crying behavior similar to that of your:

mother? _____ Yes _____ No

father? _____ Yes _____ No

If you or any of your children over six months old have never cried emotional tears, please furnish details.

Have you ever seen animals shedding emotional tears? Please specify.

Your suggestions for future research on tears and crying:

Please send to:

Dr. William H. Frey II

Dry Eye and Tear Research Center

St. Paul-Ramsey Medical Center

640 Jackson Street

St. Paul, MN 55101

Thank you for volunteering to participate in this survey.

(Permission is given to reproduce this questionnaire.)

Notes

Chapter 1. Why Do We Cry?

1. Alan Jordan and Jules Baum, "Basic Tear Flow, Does It Exist?" *Ophthalmology* 87 (September 1980): 920-30.
2. E. Treacher Collins, "The Physiology of Weeping," *British Journal of Ophthalmology* 16 (1932): 1-20.
3. Gordon Lynn Walls, *The Vertebrate Eye and Its Adaptive Radiation* (Bloomfield Hills, Mich.: Cranbrook Institute of Science, 1942), 41.
4. L. Börje Löfgren, "On Weeping," *International Journal of Psycho-Analysis* 47 (1966): 375-81.
5. Charles Darwin, *The Expression of the Emotions in Man and Animals* (London, 1872. Reprint New York: Philosophical Library, 1955), 162-75.
6. Ashley Montagu, "Natural Selection and the Origin and Evolution of Weeping in Man," *Journal of the American Medical Association* 174 (September 1960): 392-97.
7. Jona Allerhand et al., "Electrophoresis and Immunoelectrophoresis of Neonatal Tears," *The Journal of Pediatrics* 62 (January 1963): 85-92.
8. Raymond E. Records, *Physiology of the Human Eye and Visual System* (Hagerstown, Md.: Harper & Row, 1979), 37-38.
9. Stewart Duke-Elder and George Scott, *System of Ophthalmology* 12, *Neuroophthalmology* (London: Henry Kimpton, 1971), 959-66.
10. Hans Selye, *Stress Without Distress* (New York: J. B. Lippincott Co., 1964), 127 and passim.
11. Homer Smith, *From Fish to Philosopher* (New York: Doubleday & Company, 1961), 165-73.
12. Knut Schmidt-Nielsen, "The Salt-Secreting Gland of Marine Birds," *Circulation* 21 (1960): 955-67.
13. Knut Schmidt-Nielsen, "Salt Glands," *Scientific American* 200 (1959): 109-16.
14. Homer Smith, *Fish to Philosopher*, 165-73.

15. F. G. Cooch, "A Preliminary Study of the Survival Value of a Functional Salt Gland in Prairie Anatidae," *The Auk* 81 (1964): 380-393.

Chapter 2. The Source of Our Tears

1. Abraham Werb, "The Anatomy of the Lacrimal System," *The Lacrimal System,* ed. Benjamin Milder (Norwalk, Conn.: Appleton-Century-Crofts, 1983), 23-32.
2. Nicholaas van Haeringen and L. Thörig, "Enzymatic Composition of Tears," *International Tear Film Symposium—1984,* ed. Frank Holly (Lubbock, Tex.: Dry Eye Institute, 1984), 94.
3. Saiichi Mishima, "Some Physiologic Aspects of the Precorneal Tear Film," *Archives of Ophthalmology* 73 (1965): 233-41.
4. Records, *Physiology of the Human Eye,* 39-44.
5. Bernardo Weil, "The Dry Eye," *The Lacrimal System,* ed. Benjamin Milder (Norwalk, Conn.: Appleton-Century-Crofts, 1983), 118-24.
6. Gerard J. Tortora, *Principles of Human Anatomy* (New York: Harper & Row, 1983), 456-65.
7. Records, *Physiology of the Human Eye,* 37-39.
8. M. C. Seymour, ed., *Manneville's Travels* (Oxford: Clarendon Press, 1967), 208.
9. Records, *Physiology of the Human Eye,* 37-39.
10. Russell DeJong, *The Neurologic Examination* (Hagerstown, Md.: Harper & Row, 1979), 498.
11. Records, *Physiology of the Human Eye,* 37-38.
12. Stella Botelho, "Tears and the Lacrimal Gland," *Scientific American* 211 (1964): 78-86.
13. R. H. Johnson and J. M. Spalding, *Disorders of the Autonomic Nervous System* (Philadelphia: Davis Co., 1974), 216.
14. J. Daniel Nelson, telephone interview, March 1985.

Chapter 3. Shedding Tears for Science

1. Antoine Fourcroy and Louis Vauquelin, "The Chemical Examination of Tears and of the Nasal Secretion," *Annales de Chimie* 10 (1791): 113-30.
2. Records, *Physiology of the Human Eye,* 47-64.
3. Robert Brunish, "The Protein Components of Human Tears," *Archives of Ophthalmology* 57 (1957): 554-56.
4. Ulf Krause, "A Paper Electrophoretic Study on Human Tear Proteins," *Acta Ophthalmologica* Supplement 53 (1959): 1-67.

5. Olive Fedde Erickson, Rachel Hatlen, and Margaret Berg, "Lacrimal Proteins in Correlation with the Schirmer Test," *American Journal of Ophthalmology* 46 (1958): 12-21.

Chapter 4. All Tears Are Not the Same

1. Records, *Physiology of the Human Eye*, 51-52.
2. van Haeringen and Thörig, "Enzymatic Composition of Tears," 94.
3. Allan Josephson and Arnold Wald, "Enhancement of Lysozyme Activity by Anodal Tear Protein," *Proceedings of the Society of Experimental Biology and Medicine* 131 (1969): 677-79.
4. Alexander Fleming, *Proceedings of the Royal Society of London* 93B (1922): 306-17.
5. Ellen Regan, "The Lysozyme Content of Tears," *American Journal of Ophthalmology* 33 (1950): 600-05.
6. Allan Josephson and Roy Weiner, "Studies of the Proteins of Lacrimal Secretions," *Journal of Immunology* 100 (1968): 1080-92.
7. Brunish, "Protein Components," 554-56.
8. István Tapasztó, Conversation at International Tear Symposium, Lubbock, Tex., November 1984.
9. William H. Frey II et al., "Effects of Stimulus on the Chemical Composition of Human Tears," *American Journal of Ophthalmology* 92 (1981): 559-67. See also William H. Frey II, "Not-So-Idle Tears, A Lab Report," *Psychology Today* 13 (1980): 91-92; and William H. Frey II, "Crying Behavior in the Human Adult," *Integrative Psychiatry* 1 (September-October 1983): 94-100.

Chapter 5. Chemicals in Tears

1. George Page, narr., "Stress and Emotion," *The Brain* (PBS television series based on work by Richard M. Restak, 1984).
2. José Botella-Llusiá, *Endocrinology of Woman* (Philadelphia: W. B. Saunders Company, 1973), 131.
3. Harvey Guyda and Henry Friesen, "Serum Prolactin Levels in Humans from Birth to Adult Life," *Pediatric Research* 7 (1973): 534-40.
4. Janice Hastrup, Deborah Kraemer, and Robert Bornstein, "Crying Frequency of 1- to 12-year-old Boys and Girls" (Paper presented at the annual meeting of the Eastern Psychological Association, Boston, March 1985).

5. Guyda and Friesen, "Serum Prolactin Levels," 534-40.
6. Laurence Jacobs, Ida Mariz, and William Daughaday, "A Mixed Heterologous Radioimmunoassay for Human Prolactin," *Journal of Clinical Endocrinology* 34 (1972): 484-90.
7. Roland Walker, "Age Changes in the Rat's Exorbital Lacrimal Gland," *Anatomical Record* 132 (1958): 49-64.
8. Erhard Haus et al., "Chronobiological Studies of Plasma Prolactin in Women in Kyushu, Japan, and Minnesota, USA," *Journal of Clinical Endocrinology and Metabolism* 51 (1980): 632-40.
9. National Eye Registry, Portland, Oreg. (Computerized registry of drug effects on the eye). Telephone (503) 225-8456.
10. Fukashi Udaka et al., "Pathologic Laughing and Crying Treated with Levodopa," *Archives of Neurology* 41 (October 1984): 1095-96.
11. M. Peaker, J. G. Phillips, and A. Wright, "The Effect of Prolactin on the Secretory Activity of the Nasal Salt-Gland of the Domestic Duck (Anas Platyrhynchos)," *Journal of Endocrinology* 47 (1970): 123-27.
12. D. M. Ensor and J. G. Phillips, "The Effect of Environmental Stimuli on the Circadian Rhythm of Prolactin Production in the Duck (Anas Platyrhynchos)," *Journal of Endocrinology* 48 (1970): lxxi.
13. Gabor Makara, "Mechanisms by which Stressful Stimuli Activate the Pituitary-adrenal System," *Federation Proceedings* 44 (January 1985): 149-53.
14. Reinhard Jahn et al., "Adrenocorticotrophic Hormone and α-Melanocyte-Stimulating Hormone Induce Secretion and Protein Phosphorylation in the Rat Lacrimal Gland by Activation of a cAMP-Dependent Pathway," *European Journal of Biochemistry* 126 (1982): 623-29.
15. L. Rudich and F. R. Butcher, "Effects of Substance P and Elodoisin on K^+Efflux, Amylase Release and Cyclic Nucleotide Levels in Slices of Rat Parotid Gland," *Biochemical Biophysics Acta* 444 (1976): 704-11.
16. A. Nikkinen et al., "The Lacrimal Glands of the Rat and the Guinea Pig Are Innervated by Nerve Fibers Containing Immunoreactivities for Substance P and Vasoactive Intestinal Polypeptide," *Histochemistry* 81 (1984): 23-27.
17. Nicholas Plotnikoff et al., "Enkephalins: Immunomodulators," *Federation Proceedings* 44 (1985): 118-22.

18. Takashi Mizukawa et al., "Histochemistry of the Human Lacrimal Gland," *Japanese Journal of Ophthalmology* 6 (1962): 17-24.
19. John Donaldson and Frank LaBella, "Control of Free Radical Generation as the Basis for the Physiological and Pathological Roles of Manganese in Brain," *Neurotoxicology* 3 (November 1982): 146-47.
20. Ismael Mena et al., "Chronic Manganese Poisoning," *Neurology* 17 (1967): 128-36.
21. Suresh V. Chandra, "Psychiatric Illness Due to Manganese Poisoning," *Acta Psychiatric Scandanavia* 67 Supplement 303 (1983): 49-54.
22. Robert E. Gosselin et al., "Manganese Salts," *Clinical Toxicology of Commercial Products*, 5th ed. (Baltimore: Williams and Wilkins, 1984), II: 144-45.
23. István Tapasztó, "Pathophysiology of Human Tears," *International Ophthalmology Clinics* 13 (1973): 119-47.
24. William H. Frey II et al., "Prolactin, ACTH, and Leucine Enkephalin Immunoreactivity in Human Lacrimal Gland: Possible Implications for Tear Production" (Paper presented at the First International Tear Film Symposium, Lubbock, Tex., November 1984. Proceedings will be published in 1985.)

Chapter 6. Adult Crying Behavior Study

1. Dalbir Bindra, "Weeping: A Problem of Many Facets," *Bulletin of British Psychological Society* 25 (1972): 281-84.

Chapter 7. How, When, and Why Adults Cry

1. D. G. Williams, "Weeping by Adults: Personality Correlates and Sex Differences," *The Journal of Psychology* 110 (1982): 217-26.
2. William K. Lombardo et al., "Fer Cryin' Out Loud—There Is a Sex Difference," *Sex Roles* 9 (1983): 987-95.
3. Bindra, "Weeping," 281-84.

Chapter 8. Crying and Genes, Personality, Menstruation, and Depression

1. Rudolph H. Moos, "The Development of a Menstrual Distress Questionnaire," *Psychosomatic Medicine* 30 (1968): 853-67.
2. William H. Frey II et al., "Biochemical, Behavioral, and Genetic Aspects of Psychogenic Lacrimation: The Unknown

Function of Emotional Tears" (Paper presented at the First International Tear Film Symposium, Lubbock, Tex., November 1984. Proceedings of the meeting will be published in 1985.)

Chapter 9. Major Causes of Emotional Tears

1. Sandor Feldman, "Crying at the Happy Ending," *American Psychoanalytical Association Journal* 4 (1956): 477-85.
2. Jay Efran and Timothy Spangler, "Why Grown-ups Cry," *Motivation and Emotion* 3 (1979): 63-72.
3. Robert C. Bellarmine, *De Gemitu Columbae sive de Bono Lacrymarum* (Rome, 1626), 69-248.
4. Joseph de Guibert, *The Jesuits: Their Spiritual Doctrine and Practice* (Chicago: Loyola University Press, 1964), 62.
5. Arthur Koestler, *The Act of Creation* (Reprint London: Hutchinson, 1976), 273-74.
6. William F. Fry, Jr., telephone interview, May 1985 and *Encyclopedia Britannica*, Medical and Health Annual Supplement, 1984, s. v. "Laughter."
7. Norman Cousins, *Anatomy of an Illness as Perceived by the Patient* (New York: W. W. Norton & Company, 1979), 39-40.

Chapter 10. Who Says Big Boys Don't Cry?

1. Catherine E. Ross and John Mirowsky, "Men Who Cry," *Social Psychology Quarterly* 47 (1984): 138-46.
2. Williams, "Weeping by Adults," 217-26.
3. Thomas Bradbury, Lisa McDaniel, and Susan Nall, "Sex and Sex Role Differences in Crying" (Paper presented at the annual meeting of the Eastern Psychological Association, Philadelphia, April 1983).
4. Clinton J. Jesser, "Gender and Crying Among College Students" (Paper presented at the annual convention of the Midwest Sociological Society, Des Moines, Iowa, April 1982).

Chapter 11. To Cry or Not to Cry

1. Hans Selye, *The Stress of Life* (revised edition, New York: McGraw Hill, 1976), 74 and passim.
2. "2.1% Increase in Refills Pushes 1984 Rxs 1.7% Ahead of 1983," *Pharmacy Times* (April 1985), 31.
3. Karl Menninger, *The Vital Balance* (New York: The Viking Press, 1963), 138.
4. Conrad M. Riley et al., "Central Autonomic Dysfunction with Defective Lacrimation," *Pediatrics* 3 (1949): 468-78.

5. Daniel H. Funkenstein, "The Physiology of Fear and Anger," *Scientific American* 192 (May 1955): 74-80.
6. Hans Selye, *The Stress of Life*, xvi-xvii.
7. Margaret T. Crepeau, "A Comparison of the Behavior Patterns and Meanings of Weeping Among Adult Men and Women Across Three Health Conditions" (Ph.D. diss., University of Pittsburgh, 1980).
8. Merl Jackel, "The Common Cold and Depression," *Hillside Hospital Journal* xvii-2 (1968): 165-77.
9. Franz Alexander, *Psychosomatic Medicine* (New York: W.W. Norton & Co., 1950), 139, 168.
10. Leon J. Saul and C. Bernstein, "The Emotional Settings of Some Attacks of Urticaria," *Psychosomatic Medicine* 3 (1941): 349-69.
11. Joseph Kepecs, M. Robin, and M. Brunner, "Relationship between Certain Emotional States and Exudation into the Skin," *Psychosomatic Medicine* 13 (1951): 10-17.
12. Thomas M. French, "Psychogenic Factors in Asthma," *American Journal of Psychiatry* 96 (1939): 91.
13. David Maddison and Wendy L. Walker, "Factors Affecting the Outcome of Conjugal Bereavement," *British Journal of Psychiatry* 113 (October 1967): 1057-67.
14. W. Dewi Rees and Sylvia G. Lutkins, "Mortality of Bereavement," *British Medical Journal* 4 (1967): 13-16.
15. Knud J. Helsing, Moyses Szklo, and George Comstock, "Factors Associated with Mortality after Widowhood," *American Journal of Public Health* 71 (August 1981): 802-09.
16. Dianne Hales, "Psycho-immunity," *Science Digest* (November 1981): 12-14.
17. W. Dewi Rees, "Bereavement and Illness," *Journal of Thanatology* 2 (Summer-Fall 1972): 814-19.
18. Savine G. Weizman and Phyllis Kamm, *About Mourning: Support and Guidance for the Bereaved* (New York: Human Sciences Press, Inc., 1985), 37-111.
19. Savine G. Weizman and Phyllis Kamm, *When Your Mate Dies* (self-published pamphlet, 1977).
20. Kate Fuglei, telephone interviews, Fall 1983.
21. Uta Hagen, *Respect for Acting* (New York: Macmillan, 1973), 46-49.
22. William H. Schatz, *Healing a Father's Grief* (Redmond, Wash.: Medic Publishing Company, 1984), 13-14.

23. Gay Luce, *Your Second Life: Vitality and Growth in the Middle and Later Years* (New York: Delacorte Press, 1978), 71.
24. Anthony Tinn, "Everyday Coping Skills," *Northwest Orient* (Spring 1981): 16.
25. Ingeborg Day, "What Makes You Cry?" *Ms* (June 1980), 46-55.

Chapter 12. How Adults View Their Own Tears

1. Randolph R. Cornelius, "Weeping as Social Interaction" (Paper presented at the annual meeting of the Eastern Psychological Association, Baltimore, April 1982).

Chapter 13. When Others Cry

1. Harvey Jackins, *The Human Side of Human Beings* (Seattle: Rationale Island Publishers, 1974), 76, 84, 85.
2. Weizman and Kamm, *About Mourning*, 38, 113, 229, 231.
3. Ira J. Tanner, *The Gift of Grief* (New York: Hawthorn Books, Inc., 1976), 53-65.
4. Abigail McGreevy and Judy Van Heukelem, "Crying: The Neglected Dimension," *The Canadian Nurse* (January 1976): 19-21.
5. Brenda Forster and Fred Forster, "Nursing Students' Reaction to the Crying Patient," *Nursing Research* 20 (May-June 1971): 265-68.

Chapter 14. Do Animals Shed Emotional Tears?

1. Records, *Physiology of the Human Eye*, 39.
2. Darwin, *Expression of Emotions*, 165-66.
3. Cecil E. Reynolds, "The Biological Origin of Weeping," *Journal of Neurology and Psychopathology* 5 (1924-25): 355-58.
4. Ronald M. Lockley, *Grey Seal, Common Seal* (London: Andre Deutsch, 1966), 81.
5. Elaine Morgan, *The Aquatic Ape* (New York: Stein & Day, 1982), 47.
6. John E. Harkness and Marcella D. Ridgway, "Chromodacryorrhea in Laboratory Rats (Rattus Norvegicus): Etiologic Considerations," *Laboratory Animal Science* 30 (1980): 841-44.
7. Dian Fossey, *Gorillas in the Mist* (Boston: Houghton Mifflin Company, 1983), 110.
8. Elaine Morgan, *The Descent of Woman* (New York: Stein & Day, 1980), 138 and passim.
9. Elaine Morgan, *The Aquatic Ape*, 43-48 and passim.

10. Brian Davies, Letter to Langseth, 22 April 1985.
11. Montagu, "Natural Selection . . . Weeping," 392.

Chapter 15. Future Research

1. Paul C. Rosenblatt, R. Patricia Walsh, and Douglas A. Jackson, *Grief and Mourning in Cross-Cultural Perspective* (HRAF Press, 1976), 15-18.

Index

Johnson, Lyndon: 99
Jordan, Alan: 4-5

K

Kamm, Phyllis: 39, 109,
  110, 131
Kelley (Margaret H. and
  James E.) Foundation:
  27
King, Alan: 98
King, Frederick A.: 141
King Henry VI: 121
Koestler, Arthur: 92
Kraus, glands of: 17
Krause, Ulf: 25
Krishnamurti, J.: 83

L

Lacrimal glands: acinar
  secretory cells in, 48-49,
  53, 55; accessory lacrimal glands, 4, 16-17,
  20, 42; dimorphism in
  rats, 50; excretory ability, 12-14, 58; excretory
  system, 17-18; future
  research, 149; innerva-
  tion, 20; main lacrimal
  gland, 16-17, 20-22, 42,
  47-55, 58; secretory system, 16-17; *See also*
  ACTH, leucine-
  enkephalin, prolactin
Lacrimal lakes: 18

Lacrimal nucleus: 20-21,
  23
Lacrimal river: 17
Lacrimal sac: 17
Lacrimal system: excre-
  tory, 17-18; secretory,
  16-17
Lacrimators: 28-30
Lactoferrin: 42
Landon, Michael: 88
Laughter (and tears):
  94-95
Lennon, John: 90
Leucine-enkephalin: 48,
  54-55, 149
Levodopa: 51
Lewis, Jerry: 98
Lewis, John L.: 98
Limbic lobe: 21
Limbic system: 21
Lincoln, Abraham: 98
Locura manganica: 56
Lockley, Ronald M.: 136,
  139
Löfgren, L. Börje: 8
Lombardo, William: 71
Loyola, Saint Ignatius: 92
Lump in throat: 60, 73
Lutkins, Sylvia: 109
Lykken, David: 68
Lysozyme: 25, 42-44

M

Manganese: 13, 56-58
Mantle, Mickey: 97
Manz, glands of: 17
M*A*S*H: 88-89, 95

Stress: 2, 10-12, 14-15, 104-07
Stress and disease: 104-07
Substance P: 54-55, 149
Sulphuric acid: 30
Superior cervical ganglion: 22
Sympathetic center in thoracic cord: 21
Sympathetic nerve damage: 22
Sympathetic nervous system: 19, 21-22

T

Tagamet: 105
Tanner, Ira: 131
Tapasztó, István: 45-46, 56-57
Tear film: 17-18
Tears: chemicals in, 12-15, 41-58; continuous (basal), 4, 5, 21; *See also* Tear film; drug-induced, 22; Frey's theory of, 12, 26; irritant, 4, 10, 11, 17, 20, 22-26, 28-31, 34, 40-41, 43-46, 48-49, 53, 112; of joy, 87-88, 91-92; releasing, 110-13; writers and, 88; *See also* ACTH, anesthetic, animals, church, crying, crying behavior study, laughter, leucine-enkephalin, nerve damage, newborns, prolactin, retinal dazzle, theatrical tears, weeping theories
Tear studies: 24-58; collecting tears, 33; funds, 27-28; inducing emotional tears, 31-33, 35-38; inducing irritant tears, 28-31; media interest, 38-40; protein study methods, 44-45; objectives, 26, 41; precautions, 35; results, 45-46; subjects, 34; variables, 43-44; volume 33, 38, 42; *See also* ACTH, Robert Brunish, Olive Erickson, Alexander Fleming, Nicholaas van Haeringen, Ulf Krause, leucine-enkephalin, manganese, prolactin, protein, Ellen Regan
Tellegen, Auge: 79
Tennyson, Alfred Lord: 108
Terms of Endearment: 110
Thalamus: 21-22
Theatrical tears: 32, 111-113, 126
Thiopropanal S-oxide: 30
Thyroxine: 149
Tinn, Anthony: 112
Tittle, Y. A.: 97
Trigeminal (5th cranial) nerve: 20, 22; or *See* Fifth cranial nerve
Tuason, V. B.: 27, 28

TV: 74-75, 88-90
Twins: 68-69, 77-78

U

Udaka, Fukashi: 51
Ulcers: 108
Urticaria: 108

V

Valium: 105
van Haeringen, Nicholaas
 J.: 42
Van Heukelem, Judy: 132

W

Walls, Gordon Lynn: 7

Weeping: *See* Crying and
 tears
Weeping theories: 6-10, 12,
 26
Weizman, Savine: 39,
 109-10, 131
Wiemer, Marlin: 149
Williams, D. G.: 71, 79,
 100
Wolfing, glands of: 17

Y

Young, Edward; 15, 97

Z

Zung Depression Scale: 67,
 69